Keys to Reading

Theodore L. Harris
Mildred Creekmore
Louise Matteoni

Harold B. Allen
Linguistic Consultant

THE ECONOMY COMPANY
Oklahoma City   Atlanta   Indianapolis

Cover design by McRay Magleby
Cover illustration by Ron Eddington
Graphic Communications, Brigham Young University Press

ISBN 0-87892-430-2

Contents

Did You Ever?

Good Luck and Animals

All for Us

Even on a Sidewalk

Wings over Sky Ranch

Ducks, Dragons, and a King

Did You Ever?

jeep croaked maids cube beat

line

though daughter taught

caught

whip whey wheel whale

whizzed

ditch hitch catcher witch match

pitch

Molly

Aunt been

Nick

The Whizz-a-roo Pitch

After her long train ride, Molly was
very happy to see her aunt and uncle.

"My, my," said Aunt Jan. "Why, you
grow like the grass. You are so big!"

"Are you still playing ball?" asked
Uncle Nick.

"I sure am," Molly said. "I'm the
pitcher now. How about showing me your
whizz-a-roo pitch, Uncle Nick?"

"Wait, you two," said Aunt Jan.
"The apples may need to be picked
before you play ball. They have been
big and red for a few days now."

The next day Molly and Uncle Nick played ball. Molly caught just about every ball.

They played near the apple trees by the walk. Each tree had big red apples on it. All of the apples looked very good to Molly.

After they played catch, Molly again asked her uncle to show her the whizz-a-roo pitch. "Soon," he said. Molly let the ball fall to the ground. She did not want to wait.

The next day Aunt Jan went to town, and Uncle Nick went fishing. He took his fishing rod and fishing line. He wanted to catch some fish for lunch.

Molly was all alone. She took her ball outside. She walked behind the house and sat down. Then she began to pitch the ball into the air and catch it.

"A whizz-a-roo pitch would be way over the house," Molly thought.

Molly looked at the roof. It was very high. "I think I can," she said. She took two steps back. "Here goes the whizz-a-roo!"

Up, up the ball whizzed. Then over the house the ball flew.

"Say, a ball just about hit me on the head!" someone said.

Molly ran around the house. Some men had picked a few of her uncle's apples. But one man was holding her ball.

"Is this your ball?" he asked Molly.

"Yes," Molly said.

"Did you throw it over the house?" he asked.

"Yes," said Molly.

"That was some throw!" the man said.

"Did it hurt you?" Molly asked.

"No," he said, "I just about caught it."

"You must be Sam's girl," the man said.

"Sam is not my dad!" Molly said.

"Isn't this Sam's farm?" the man asked.

"No, it is my uncle's farm," Molly said.
"His name is Nick. I have only been here
for two days."

"Nick!" the man said. Then he turned
to the other men. "Stop! We are
at the wrong place."

The man looked at Molly. "Thank you
for helping us. That good throw saved
your uncle's apples."

"That was a whizz-a-roo pitch," she said.

"I would call it an apple pitch," the
man said.

And later Uncle Nick said the same thing.

"We'll call that the apple pitch. It
saved the apples."

Then Uncle Nick baked a big apple pie
for Molly.

smallest biggest oldest smartest

chance prince dodge

fill hats met

its him left dolls cast

keeper smaller louder

brushed pointed stayed

wide save woke

fine joke mean meet

Sight words.

building doctor

living McBean

Sound the words.

longest

else

track

well

longer

moaned

note

wife

morning

Mr. McBean's Train

13

For days little Mr. McBean had not been well. So one morning he went to see his doctor.

"Mr. McBean, it's time for you to slow down," said the doctor. "You must stop building big things. Think about building little things. Then you'll get well."

"Oh, my!" moaned Mr. McBean. He left the doctor and went home to his big house and his little wife.

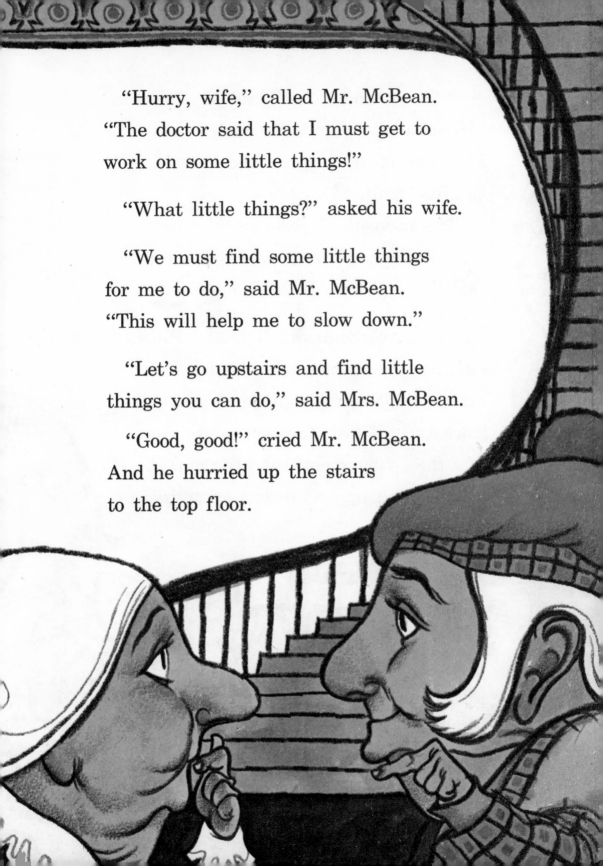

"Hurry, wife," called Mr. McBean. "The doctor said that I must get to work on some little things!"

"What little things?" asked his wife.

"We must find some little things for me to do," said Mr. McBean. "This will help me to slow down."

"Let's go upstairs and find little things you can do," said Mrs. McBean.

"Good, good!" cried Mr. McBean. And he hurried up the stairs to the top floor.

"I found something!" said Mr. McBean.
"Here's a little old train in this box.
I'll make it the biggest, the longest,
the best train of all!"

"The biggest! The longest!" cried
Mrs. McBean. "Now you know the doctor
said to work with little things."

But Mr. McBean didn't hear. He was
building the train track. And he kept
making it longer and longer. Soon the
track ran all over the house. It ran
into the living room, the bedroom, the
kitchen, and up and down the stairs.

Then little Mr. McBean went to the bedroom. He ran the train from his bed. He made it stop and go. He turned the lights on and off. And he made the train go who-ooh, who-ooh!

"Now there is nothing else for me to do," moaned Mr. McBean.

"Run the train!" said his wife.

"It's no fun now," moaned Mr. McBean. "I must get up and make a longer track."

"No," said Mrs. McBean. "The doctor said you'll have to slow down and think about little things."

17

Mrs. McBean went downstairs to the kitchen. "Oh!" she said. "Here's something we can do!"

Mrs. McBean wrote a note. She put it on the train. The note said, "Would you like a glass of milk?"

The little train left the kitchen and took the note around the living room and up to the bedroom. Mr. McBean saw the note. Then he wrote a note to his wife. It said, "Yes, I would like some milk, and some cake, too."

Now there was something else to do with the little train!

18

One morning the doctor came to see
Mr. McBean.

"Hello, Doctor," said Mr. McBean.
"I'm building little things. Sit down,
and I'll show you."

Mr. McBean wrote a note. Then he
pushed a button. The doctor watched
the train come up the track.

Mr. McBean put the note on the train
and pushed the button again.

The doctor laughed and laughed when
the train came back with milk and cake.

"Soon I'll be well!" said Mr. McBean.
Then he gave the doctor some milk.

Once I Made a Train

I made a train with boxes,
With cans and skates and string.
I even put a bell on top—
My train had everything!

I pushed my train along the track.
It started very well,
But all at once my sister came
To take away the bell.
Then Mother took the cans away,
My brother took the string,
My dad took skates and boxes,
They didn't leave a thing!

Once I had a little train
That started down the track,
But then it met my family
And it never did come back!

by Kathryn Jones

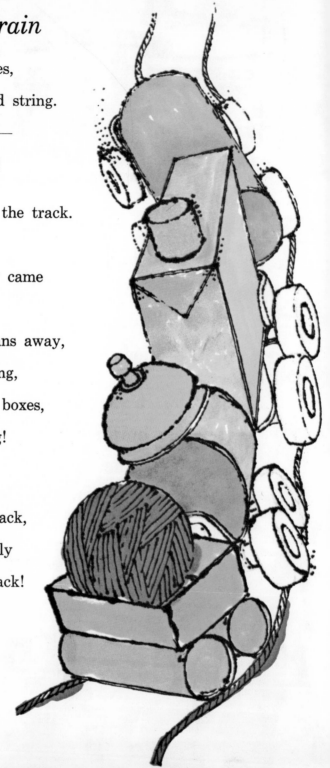

today   slay   lay

hay

leg   leaves   lucky

led

wake   wagon   wing

week

happening   coffee   summer

burro

sister

Pedro

Pedro and the Burro

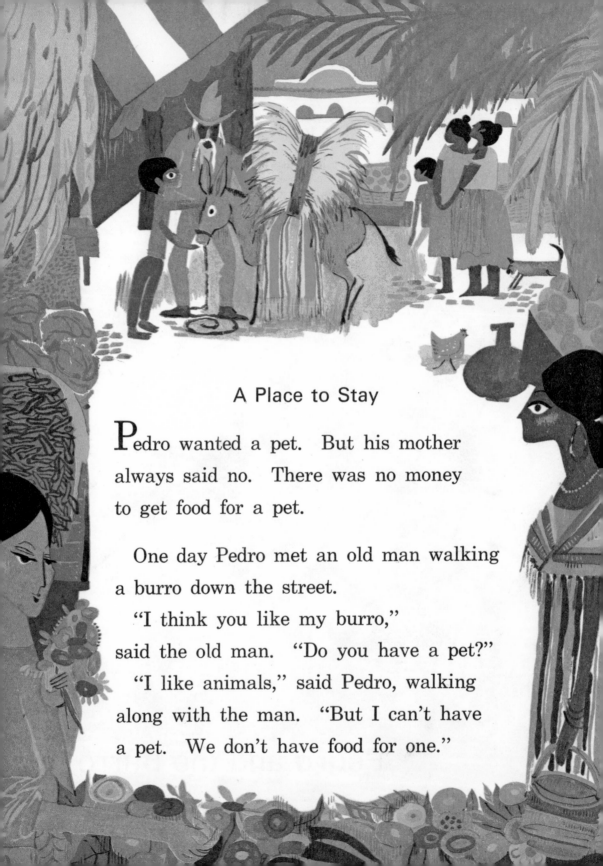

A Place to Stay

Pedro wanted a pet. But his mother
always said no. There was no money
to get food for a pet.

One day Pedro met an old man walking
a burro down the street.
"I think you like my burro,"
said the old man. "Do you have a pet?"
"I like animals," said Pedro, walking
along with the man. "But I can't have
a pet. We don't have food for one."

"Would you like to keep my burro
for a week?" asked the old man.
"I will give you some hay."

"It would make me very happy,"
said Pedro. "Let's go ask my mother."

Pedro led the way to his home.
"Mother, Mother!" he called.
"Now I have a pet!"

"Pedro, you know we don't have
money for pet food," said his mother.

Then the old man said, "I'm going
away for a week. I will leave some hay."

"Sit down and eat some lunch while
I think about it," said Mother.

After lunch Mother said, "We'll keep
the burro for a week. But no longer!"

What a happy week Pedro had!
He brushed and brushed the little burro.
He led him for walks around the park.
And Pedro always let his little sister
ride the burro home. "He is so much
fun to ride," Pedro's sister said.
"I like the way he walks."

Soon the week came to an end. But the
old man didn't come back for his burro.
"What can we do?" Mother cried.
"I don't have the money to get more hay.
And the old man may never come back!"

face	fireplace	racing	cent	cents
	gust	gold	gown	gets
	news	nap	nights	neck
seed	class	story	bags	visit
hi	hills	hears	hustle	hat

Sight words.

many　taken

Pedro Looks for a Way

Two more days went by. The old man had not come for his burro. And all the burro's hay was gone. Pedro didn't know what to do.

"Let's go to the park," Pedro said to his sister. "This may be one of our last walks with the burro."

Pedro and his sister saw many people
in the park. One man was showing a
big hat to the people around him.

"Pictures taken in a big hat!"
he called. And many people put on
the big hat while he took pictures.

"Could my little girl have
her picture taken on your burro?"
a lady asked Pedro.

"Oh, yes," said Pedro. He led the
burro over to the little girl so
the man could take her picture.

Soon many people wanted to get
pictures taken with the burro.
One lady put her arm around
the little burro's neck.
One after the other, children sat
on his back.

Every time the man took a picture,
he gave Pedro ten cents.

"Will you visit the park every day?"
asked the man. "I will give you ten
cents for each picture, and I will see
that the burro gets some hay."

Pedro hurried home to tell his mother.
He had found a way to keep a pet!

But at his house, Pedro found the
old man talking to his mother.

"I had a visit with your mother,"
said the old man. "How is the burro?"

Pedro told him about the man
in the park and the ten cents.

"But now you have come back
for the little burro," said Pedro.

"No," said the man. "I must
go away again. I came back to find
a home for the little burro."

"May I keep him?" asked Pedro.
"I have a way to get hay for him."

"It is for your mother to say,"
said the old man.

Pedro's mother put one arm around the
little burro's neck. Then she put her
other arm around Pedro. "I say
that Pedro gets a pet!" she said.

clean   doctor's   cool

crane   beams   skate   smile

chuck   dots   grin   ill

sideways   raining   wheels

skinny   gutter   worry

cart

ropes

dutch

peanut

Peggy

Saturday

Fay

shoes   strangers   double

Double Dutch

29

One Saturday morning Fay came running
out of the apartment house. Mr. Sam was
outside his store, shining the window.

"Hello, Fay!" called Mr. Sam. "What
do you need? Cat food? Milk for the
baby?"

"No!" Fay said, laughing. "It's my
birthday, and Mother gave me some money.
And I got new red shoes, too!"

"Happy birthday!" said Mr. Sam. "What
are you going to do with your money?"

Fay pointed to a long rope at the back of the store. "I want the biggest and longest rope I can get. I'm going to jump double dutch all day," she said.

"You'll wear out your new shoes in just one day!" Mr. Sam laughed. Then he cut off a long rope for Fay. "What else can I do for you?"

"Nothing else, thanks," she said.

Fay ran to the park with her rope. She saw Peggy and Jane talking to the balloon man. But the girls came running when they saw Fay. Peggy pointed to the new rope.

"Did you get the rope for your birthday?" Peggy asked.

"Yes," said Fay. "Come and jump double dutch with me."

Peggy and Fay turned the rope. Jane
was tall and skinny, but she could jump
like a rabbit! Peggy and Fay made
the double rope fly!

"Jump around the sun, jump around the
moon, jump around the peanut cart, and
slide on a balloon!" the girls called.

They jumped rope for a long time.
Then Jane and Peggy had to go home.

"Thanks, Fay," said Jane. "I wish
I had a rope like that."

"Well, this rope is longer than I
need," Fay said. "I'll give you and
Peggy some of it."

The girls ran to see Mr. Sam.

"What's this?" he asked. "Cut up your rope? Soon you'll have no rope, Fay!" But he cut off a rope for Jane and a rope for Peggy. And both girls ran out the door with the new ropes.

Fay went back to the park. But Jane and Peggy didn't come back. Later Fay saw a girl playing alone. So she walked over to the girl.

"I'm Fay. Who are you?" she asked.

"I'm Beth, and I'm just moving in over there," the girl said. She pointed to a tall apartment building.

"Do you want to jump rope?" Fay asked. "I got this rope for my birthday."

"Thanks!" Beth said. "It's my birthday, too."

"I guess it's bad to have a birthday when you are moving," said Fay.

"Mother said I can have a party later," said Beth. "But a birthday is no fun with strangers all around."

Fay laughed. "We won't be strangers for long! Come on!"

Then Fay put one end of her rope around a skinny tree. She turned the rope while Beth jumped.

Fay called, "Jump around the sun, jump around the moon, jump around the peanut cart, and slide on a balloon!"

Later Fay said, "Come with me, Beth. I want you to have something for your birthday. Let's go see Mr. Sam."

When they got to the store, Fay asked Mr. Sam to cut her rope again.

"If I cut your rope again, you can't jump double dutch," said Mr. Sam.

"We can if we have two ropes," Fay said. And she gave one rope to Beth.

"Thank you!" Beth said. "I'll see you soon!" And she ran home.

But no one came to the park the next few days. Fay came each day with her rope. But Jane and Peggy didn't come. And Beth didn't come with her rope.

"I'll never get to jump double dutch again," thought Fay.

On Saturday a week later, Fay went to the store for milk.

"I'm glad to see you," Mr. Sam said. His eyes were shining. "I have something for you. It's from your new friend."

"From Beth?" Fay asked.

"Yes, she has been looking for you," said Mr. Sam. He put his hand in his pocket. "Here it is. You'll find a note inside."

Can you guess what the note said?

We work with words.

cookie brownie

clock cleaners clumping close

globe glide glance

skunk's boy's dragon's ranch's

today newspapers haircuts

Sound the words.

Tillie

class

gloomy

doctor's

zookeeper

chimpanzee

hospital

runaway

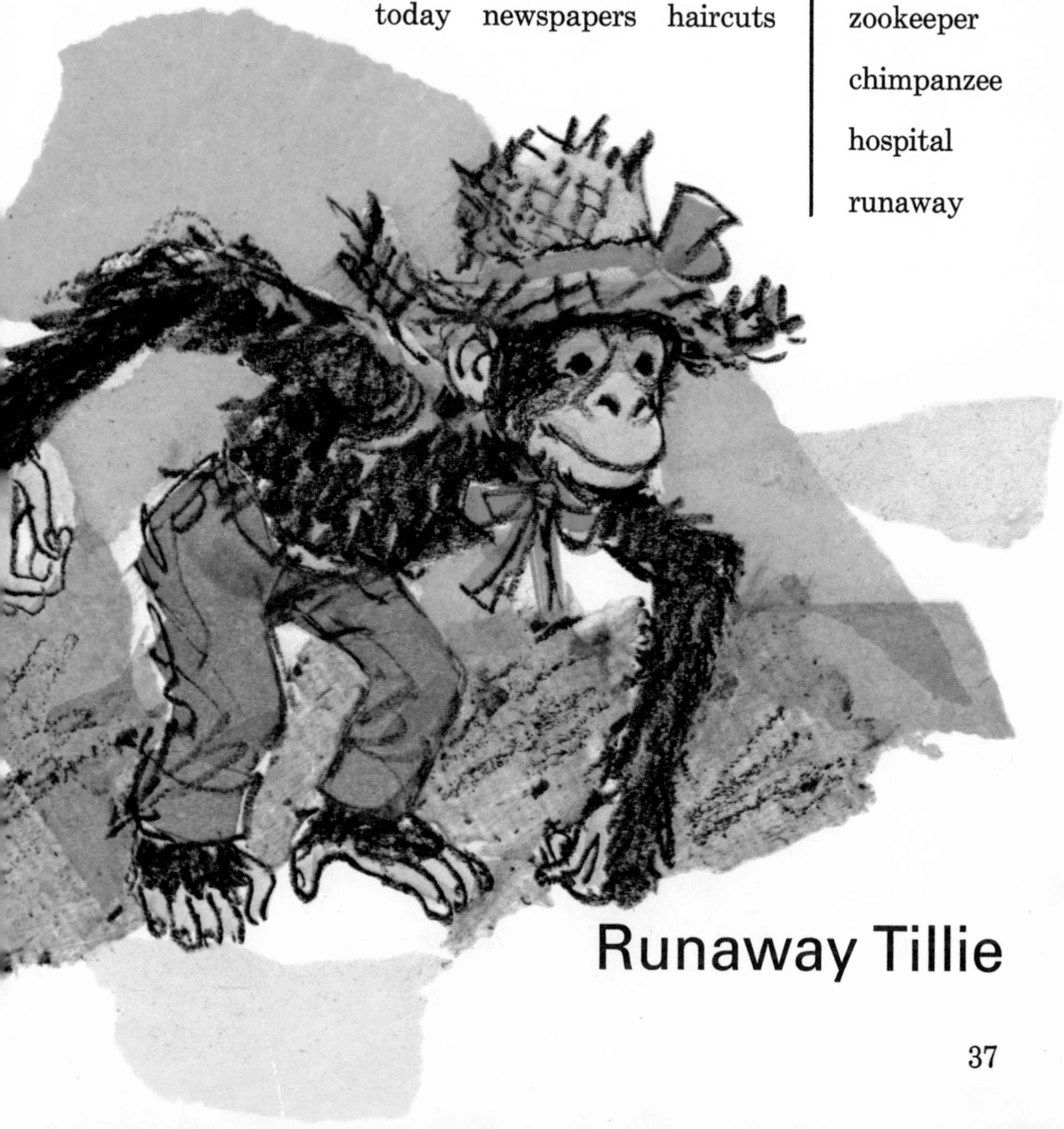

Runaway Tillie

One day Tillie didn't get up to
play with the children. The little
chimpanzee stayed on her bed of hay.
So the zookeeper called the doctor.

When the doctor came, he found Tillie
in bed. Her head was under a quilt.
The doctor took away the quilt to look
at her.

"How gloomy you are!" he said.
"Are you sick, Tillie?"

Tillie stayed very still. The doctor
tried to find out what was wrong.

"I can't tell what's wrong," he said.
"There's just one thing to do.
We must take Tillie to the animal
hospital right away."

"I'll carry her," said the zookeeper.
So he put the quilt around her and took
her to the doctor's car. Tillie stayed
very still all the way to the hospital.

First of all, the doctor put
a white gown on Tillie. Then he led
the zookeeper out of the hospital room.
Tillie watched them go. Now she
was all alone. And she was afraid!

Tillie looked at the doctor's room.
She saw a box with blinking lights
and a glass that went gurgle, gurgle.
There were green wires and black wires.
And Tillie didn't like the white gown.
She wanted to get out of there!

The little chimpanzee jumped
to the floor. Then she ran out the door.
Right away she felt better.

When she went into the room next door,
Tillie was surprised. There were dogs
everywhere! And they all looked gloomy.

How surprised the dogs were to see
Tillie! She walked to the first dog.
He gave a loud bark. Then he ran round
and round. Tillie wanted to help.
So she opened the little door, and
the dog ran out.

All the dogs began to bark and bark.
Tillie opened all the doors. The dogs
jumped to the floor and ran after her!

Tillie's keeper heard the noise.
"Come back, Tillie!" he called.
But Tillie ran on. She was trying
to get away from the dogs.

All at once Tillie saw an open window.
She forgot that she was sick.
So out the window she went!

Tillie ran fast to get away from
the hospital. She ran until she came
to a school. The doors were open.
So she walked in and looked around.
Soon she came to a class of boys and
girls. The teacher was gone.

"There's a chimpanzee!" cried a girl.
The surprised class called to Tillie.
So she went into the room, picked up a
stick, and jumped up and down. This
was much more fun than the hospital!

"I'll give that runaway chimpanzee
something to eat," said a boy. And he
gave Tillie an apple.

Other children in the class gave her
food, and soon Tillie felt even better.

All at once there was no noise.
The class sat down. A teacher was at
the door. Tillie looked at the teacher.
Tillie wanted to get out of there!

So the runaway chimpanzee jumped out
the window. She ran and ran until
she bumped into a man.

"Tillie! Come back!" called the man.

It was Tillie's keeper! She stopped
and put her arms around his neck.
Tillie felt much better now!

"Runaway Tillie!" said the keeper.
"I don't think you're sick at all.
You're going right back to the zoo!"

GOOD
LUCK AND
ANiMALS

boy's	join	noises	cowboy	voice
	doesn't	he'll	wasn't	who's
	grew	stew	threw	news	newspaper
	smart	smallest	smoke	smile
	spider	speak	spinning	spend
start	stool	standing	stored	story
	gust	land	crisp	clock	skunk

Mother Skunk's Moving Day

45

Mother Skunk sat looking at her four
new babies.

"Our family must find a new home," she
told Father Skunk. "The people in the
big house saw you last night. So we
can't spend another night here."

"I heard a loud voice say that skunks
bring good money," said Father Skunk.
"We must hurry before we are found."

"Then let's get moving today!"
said Mother Skunk.

"Where will we find a new home?"
asked Father Skunk.

"I have found a spot," said Mother
Skunk. "It's in a nice part of the woods.
And it's on the other side of the highway."

"Who's going to carry the babies to
the woods?" asked Father Skunk.

"I'll take them," said Mother Skunk.

The skunks didn't spend time sleeping
that day. Mother Skunk worked all day
on the new home. She dug a hole by a
stump. Then she put some grass in it.
Now she could go back for her family.

One by one, Mother Skunk took
her babies to the side of the road.
Father Skunk stayed there with them.

Then Mother Skunk picked up one baby
in her mouth and started slowly across
the highway. Just as she walked out
on the highway, two cars drove up.

Mother Skunk didn't stop,
but the cars did!

Mother Skunk hid the first baby in
some tall grass. Then she started
back for the next one.

Soon many cars had stopped.
Horns were blowing.

"Who's holding us up?" called out
one driver in a gloomy voice.

More and more cars had to stop.
More and more horns were blowing.
Then a black and white car drove up
beside the other cars.

"What's wrong here?" a policeman
called in a loud voice.

The driver of a milk truck pointed
to Mother Skunk. She was walking across
the highway with a baby in her mouth.

"Well, how about that!" said the
policeman with a smile.

Then the policeman drove slowly
along the highway. He couldn't hide
a smile as he said to each driver,
"You'll have to wait. A family is
moving across the highway."

"Who's moving?" asked a driver.

"Someone has taken pictures of the family," said the policeman. "Look for the story in the newspaper."

At last all the babies were across the highway. Then Father Skunk went across. Now Mother Skunk's family was across, and the cars could go.

The next day people saw the story "Mother Skunk's Moving Day" in the morning newspaper. The best part was the picture of Mother Skunk holding a sleeping baby in her mouth.

brings   brush   brook

cricket   croaked   cream

frame   frog's   front

capture   furniture   mixture

cleaners   clang   club

sleeps   slice   slick

safe   drive   pile

Carlos   country   deer

branch

creek

free

pasture

climb

slip

Lee

fawn

Carlos Goes to the Country

On a High Hill

Carlos looked out the window of the bus.
His city home was far behind him
now. He saw nothing but country.

"Mom said Lee would meet me at the
bus stop," Carlos thought. "I'll be
glad to see her again. Lee knows
many good things to do."

When the bus stopped, Carlos saw
Lee standing outside. She shouted a
big hello as she ran up to meet him.
A week with Lee was going to be fun!

It didn't take long to get to the
farm. But Lee didn't give Carlos time
to see the house. She wanted to show
him around.

"Come on, Carlos!" she said.
"You can't spend your week in the country
just standing here. Come on!"

Lee led Carlos to a high hill. Then
they began to climb.

"Climb sideways, and you won't slip,"
Lee said.

So Carlos climbed the hill sideways.
From the top he saw the sun shining on
a woods and cattle in a big pasture.
And he saw what looked like the best
creek that ever was!

"Do you see the cattle in the pasture?"
Lee asked. "We are having a roundup
today. It's going to be fun. If you like,
you can go on the roundup, too."

But Carlos didn't say a thing
about the roundup. He just looked
at the creek.

"Forget the roundup!" Lee laughed.
"Go on down to the creek, Carlos.
I'll go back and get you a fishing rod."

"Oh, boy! I always wanted to fish
in a creek like that!" Carlos said.

Carlos ran down to the creek.

"Lee knows just what I like
to do!" he thought.

Then all at once Carlos heard a
noise. It came from the hill behind
him. What could it be?

Again Carlos heard the noise. He turned around and saw a white baby deer. It was coming down a high trail. And all at once its feet began to slip. Then it fell down the side of the hill and into a tree. It caught two legs on a branch of the tree. The baby deer began to kick. But it could not kick its legs free of the branch!

"Lee isn't here," Carlos thought. "I'll have to find a way to free the fawn." So he left the creek and climbed sideways up the hill.

chief field piece

strong stretch stripe

throat thrash threw

mind finding child

hire wired spire

Blanco

believe

stretched

thrashing

wild

fire

The White Fawn

When Carlos went up the hill,
the white baby deer was thrashing
about on the tree branch.
"What can I do?" Carlos thought.

He watched the fawn give a
wild kick, trying to get free.
Two legs were caught on the branch.
"I believe I can climb to that
branch," thought Carlos.

The fawn gave a wild kick.

"If I can get to the first branch, I believe I can climb it," Carlos thought.

Carlos stretched and stretched until he caught hold of the branch. He put his legs around it and began to climb.

The fawn was still thrashing about. Carlos saw two cuts on its legs.

"Don't be afraid, little one," Carlos said kindly. "Don't be afraid, Blanco. I'll find a way to help you."

But the fawn gave another wild kick. Carlos was afraid it might slip and fall sideways down the hill.

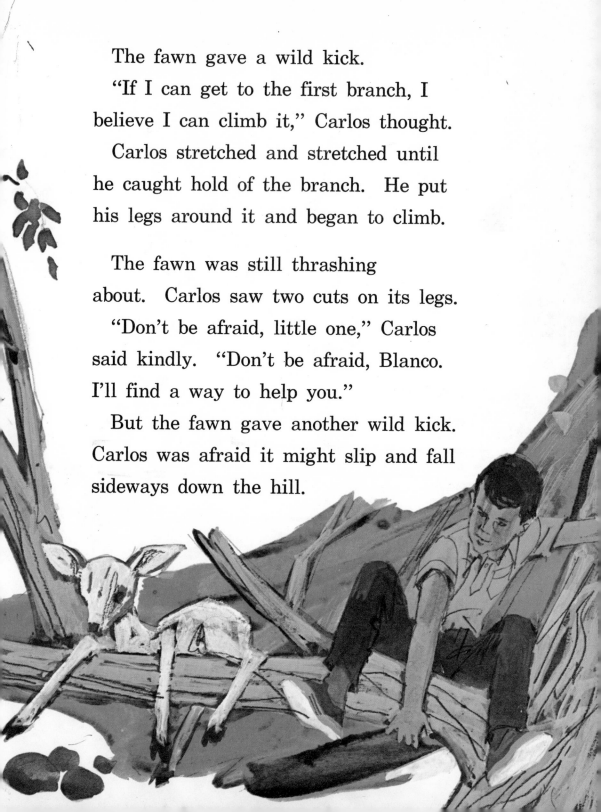

Then Carlos thought of a story he had heard at school. It was about a horse that was afraid of fire. A man put something over the eyes of the horse and led it away from the fire.

"I'll take off my shirt and put it over Blanco's eyes," thought Carlos. "I believe it might help him, too."

"Don't be afraid, Blanco," said Carlos, as he put the shirt over Blanco's eyes. He talked kindly to Blanco all the time. Carlos put the fawn under his arm and climbed down. Then he put his shirt around the cuts on Blanco's legs.

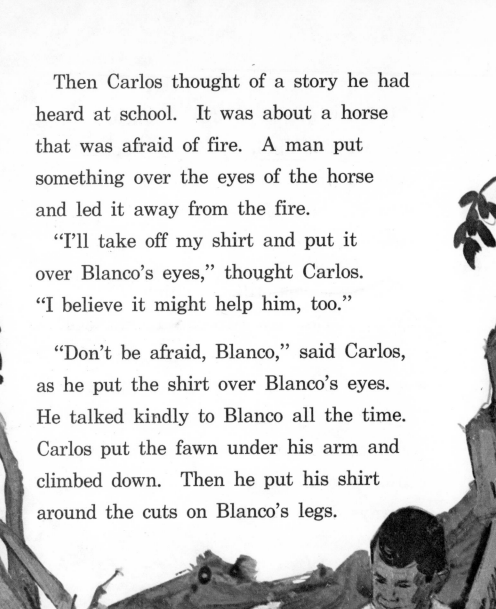

Just then Lee came running back
with the fishing rod. How surprised
she was to see Carlos with a fawn
under his arm!

"Where did you find that baby
deer?" she asked.

"You won't believe me," Carlos said.
"I found him in a tree!
His legs were caught on a branch.
I'm going to call him Blanco."

"Blanco?" asked Lee. "I don't know
what that means."

"Blanco means white," Carlos said.

"What a good name for him!" Lee said.
"We can take him to the house until
his legs get better. But I'll take him
if you want to go fishing."

"I can fish some other time," Carlos
said. "Now I want to help Blanco.
I can't wait to tell my family all
about my first day on your farm.
Why, the country is even better than
I thought!"

Think about This:

What do you think Carlos and Lee will do
with Blanco when he is well?

nature   future   creature

capture

crisp   crouch   cracker   crossed

cricket

firehouse   haircuts   outdoors

fireplace

blind   mild   minded

mind

plum   plump   plants

plan

stack   starts   stood

stool

list   hum   rock   send

luck

they're   hadn't   where's

wasn't

together   any

A Groundhog by the Fireplace

Mr. Rabbit put on his hat and red
shoes and hopped down the road.

"Where are you going today?" asked
Miss Squirrel.

"I'm off to capture a cricket," said
Mr. Rabbit. "Last winter I had bad luck.
But this winter I'll have good luck
if I put a cricket by the fireplace."

"If you ask me, good luck and crickets
don't go together," said Miss Squirrel.

"Well, I plan to capture a cricket!"
said Mr. Rabbit as he hopped away.

Mr. Rabbit found other bugs, but
he didn't find a cricket.

"That's bad!" said Mr. Rabbit.

"What's bad?" asked a deep voice.
There beside a tree sat a big groundhog.

"I can't capture a cricket," said
Mr. Rabbit. "And I want one to sit
by my fireplace. It brings good luck."

Mr. Groundhog thought about this.
After a while he asked, "Do you know
that a groundhog by the fireplace
brings more good luck than a cricket?
I'll sit by your fireplace."

"Thanks, Mr. Groundhog,"
said Mr. Rabbit.

On the way home, Mr. Rabbit met
Miss Squirrel. He told her that
Mr. Groundhog brings good luck.

"If you ask me, good luck and
groundhogs don't go together,"
said Miss Squirrel.

"Well, I plan to try Mr. Groundhog
and see," said Mr. Rabbit.

Mr. Rabbit got his dinner ready when
he got to his house.

"Get some for me!" said Mr. Groundhog.

"Don't you just sit by the fireplace
the way crickets do?" asked Mr. Rabbit.

"Oh no! Groundhogs eat every day,"
said Mr. Groundhog.

The groundhog ate and ate and ate.
There wasn't much left for Mr. Rabbit.

"If groundhogs bring good luck,
I don't mind eating a small dinner,"
thought Mr. Rabbit.

Then Mr. Rabbit hopped into the
living room to sit by the fire.
But the groundhog was sitting
in Mr. Rabbit's big rocking chair.

"Won't you sit on that little stool
by the fireplace as crickets do?"
asked Mr. Rabbit.

"A groundhog must have a nice,
big chair," said Mr. Groundhog.
And he went on rocking in the chair.
So Mr. Rabbit sat on the stool.

Later Mr. Rabbit went upstairs
to his bedroom. Mr. Groundhog came
upstairs, too.

"Don't you sleep by the fireplace
the way crickets do?" asked Mr. Rabbit.

"No, it hurts a groundhog to sleep on
the floor. I must have a nice bed and
a warm quilt," said Mr. Groundhog.

So Mr. Rabbit went to sleep on the
floor that night.

"I'm cold and my back hurts and
I need more to eat!" cried Mr. Rabbit
the next morning. "But I don't mind,
if a groundhog brings me good luck!"

Days went by. Mr. Groundhog got fat.
Mr. Rabbit got thin.

Every day Mr. Rabbit said, "I don't
need any more luck, Mr. Groundhog."

But Mr. Groundhog went on eating
and sitting and rocking by the fireplace.

One day a very thin and gloomy
Mr. Rabbit went to see Miss Squirrel.

"If you ask me," said Miss Squirrel,
"I don't think groundhogs and good luck
go together."

"That's right," said Mr. Rabbit.
"But is there any way to make him leave?"

"I'll help," said Miss Squirrel.
"Let's go to your house."

When they got there, the groundhog was sleeping by the fireplace.

"If he were a little cricket, we could throw him outside," said Mr. Rabbit.

"We can't throw him, but we can move him," said Miss Squirrel. She picked up two fat legs. Mr. Rabbit picked up two fat arms. And together they took Mr. Groundhog outside.

"Thanks for the help, Miss Squirrel," said Mr. Rabbit. "The groundhog wasn't lucky for me. But I'm lucky to have you for a friend."

"If you ask me, good luck and friends go together!" said Miss Squirrel.

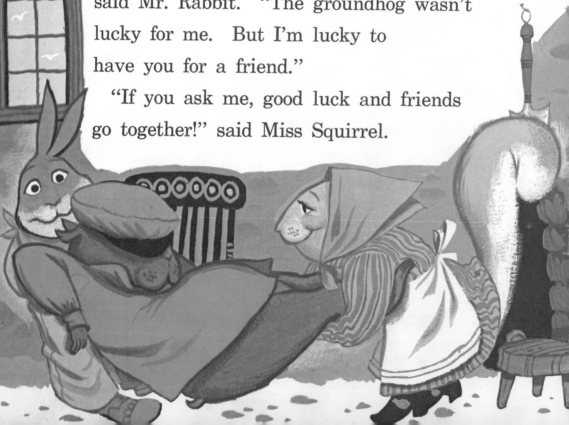

sore tore stores wore

dirt burn serve

wake safe drive

drop leg ranch sing

clean jokes smiled cube

brave brother break

live hungry

stored

burrow

pile

nuts

leaves

brush

When Winter Comes

Do you live where it is cold in winter?
If you do, you may plan to play outside
some days. If there is snow, you might
plan to make a snowman.

If it's too cold to make a snowman,
you can stay inside and be warm. And
in a home like yours, you can find
something to eat.

But what if you were an animal in
the woods? How would you get ready
for winter?

A rabbit doesn't live in a warm house like yours. He makes a bed in tall grass or in a brush pile. The brush pile helps to keep out the snow. The rabbit likes to have his bed near green sticks. When he gets hungry, he can eat bark from the green sticks.

The squirrel makes his winter home in a hole in a tree. There he makes a bed of leaves and grass. He puts some nuts in the tree, too. He can eat the stored nuts when he gets hungry.

The beaver makes his home in a pond.
He puts sticks together with mud. A
beaver puts his food under the water
so he can swim down for it when
he is hungry.

The chipmunk doesn't like the cold.
He will sleep all winter in a burrow he
dug under the ground. The chipmunk will
put a pile of food beside his bed of
leaves in the burrow. Now and then he
will eat a few stored nuts and then
go back to sleep.

What do you know about other animals?
How will they spend the winter?

ought brought trough   cough

brother become sometimes   front

fold older mold   gold

spark grasp spill   spider

throne thread throwing   throat

swimmer sweep sway   swimming

grandfather sidewalk newspapers   outdoors

hi

The Present That Croaked

It was Saturday. Billy hurried
down the street.

"I can take all the time I need to
get a birthday present for Dad," Billy
thought. "I want to give him a real
surprise. Not a store present. I'll
do my shopping outdoors."

Billy saw a spider going up a wall.
"Maybe Dad would like a spider,"
Billy thought. "He's a teacher, and
he could take it to school."

But the spider ran over the wall.
"Oh well, a spider would run away
and not be much fun," thought Billy.

In the park Billy saw a squirrel
taking nuts up a tree.

"A squirrel sleeps all winter,"
thought Billy. "That's not a good
present."

Then Billy saw a bus coming down
the street. "That's the River Road bus,"
he thought. "I'll take it, and then I
can look for something at the river."
So Billy sat by the window. He
watched the city turn into country as
they came near the river. Soon the
bus made a turn at River Road.

Billy got off the bus and ran to the
river. He stretched out on a big rock
to watch the water. He saw some
gold leaves float by. Then he saw
fish swimming along.

"I don't think fish are friendly,"
he said. "So I won't try to catch one."

Billy took off his shoes and walked
along the river. The mud and
cold water felt good on his feet.
He looked into the water. Right in
front of him was a big, green frog.
It sat on a rock, blinking at Billy.

"Hi, Mr. Frog! Tell me, are you
friendly?" Billy asked.

"Croak!" said the frog.

"Well, Mr. Frog!" said Billy.
"You're talking to me, but I don't know
what that croak means."

Then the frog's neck began to look
like a balloon. He croaked again.

"Say, you're nice!" said Billy.
"And you're just right for a present."
Billy stretched out his arm. Slowly
he put his hand around the frog.
It felt cold and wet, but Billy held on.
"Croak!" went the frog.

"Oh, I won't hurt you, Mr. Frog,"
said Billy. "How can I get you home?
I guess I'll put you under my shirt."
The frog's feet felt funny under
Billy's shirt. But he thought, "Dad
will like having a frog and taking
it to his school!"

Billy patted the frog under his shirt
as he was going home on the bus.

"I'll make a home for Mr. Frog in a
box," thought Billy.

"Croak!" went the frog. Billy patted
the front of his shirt again.

When Billy walked in the back door,
his mother and father were sitting
in the living room.

"Is that you, Billy?" called Dad.

"Hi!" said Billy from the kitchen.

"Where have you been?" asked Dad.

"Down by the river," said Billy.
"Say, Dad, do you have many animals
at your school?"

"No, not now," said Dad. "We need
more. Did you find something?"

Before Billy could talk, the frog
croaked. The front of Billy's shirt
popped out.

Billy held on to the front of his
shirt and coughed and coughed.

"Billy, what's wrong?" asked Mother.

"I have a frog in my throat," he said,
as he walked into the living room.

"Where did you get a bad cough
like that?" she asked.

"I must have caught it at the river,"
said Billy. Then he began to smile.

"That's nothing to smile about!"
said Mother. "We don't want you to get
a bad throat."

Just then the frog croaked again.
"Croak!" Billy had to cough again.

Dad put down his newspaper and called to Billy. "Come over here. What do you have under your shirt?"

"Oh, Dad," moaned Billy. "I wanted to wait until your birthday."

Billy put his hand inside his shirt. He caught two of the frog's long, skinny legs. Then he walked over to his dad.

"Happy birthday!" said Billy.

"A frog!" said Dad, looking surprised. "Is this the frog in your throat?"

Then Dad started to laugh. Now Billy could laugh, too.

"I did my shopping outdoors this time," said Billy.

"He's a very nice present," said Dad. "I'll take him to school. But after that let's take him back to the river. I think a frog is better off by a river where he can go swimming. You won't mind, will you?"

"No, Dad. I won't mind at all," said Billy. "Happy birthday!"

Think about This:

What other presents might Billy have found when he was shopping outdoors?
What kind of teacher was Billy's dad?

ALL
FOR
US

sailor	owner	dollar		mayor
marine	sardine	magazine		machine
those	cloth	without	these	weather
	should	wash	shear	shook
	sigh	bright	mighty	nights
smiling	smartest	smooth		smiled
	split	splint	splatter	splashing
ant's	Ben's	dragon's	Jeff's	Rod's

Rain for Rod

It was hot in the city where Rod
lived. The weather had been hot for
the longest time. No rain had come.
The nights were as hot as the days.

"Why won't it rain?" asked Rod's
friends. "It's so hot!"

The boys took off their shoes. But
still it was hotter and hotter. The
boys got short haircuts. But the
haircuts didn't help a bit.

One day Rod thought about his
birthday. So he went to his mother
and asked, "Isn't Dad a weatherman?"

"Yes," Mother said.

"And isn't Saturday my birthday?"
asked Rod. Mother nodded.

"Then I know what I want Dad to do
for my birthday," said Rod. "I want
him to make it rain for me!"

Mother was surprised. "You want Dad
to make it rain?" she asked.

"Yes," Rod said. "The city won't let
us turn on the water in the street.
But if it will rain, we can go
splashing again."

"Well, Dad is a good weatherman,"
said Mother. "But I don't think he can
make it rain."

"What good is a weatherman if he
can't make weather!" Rod said.

That night Rod was watching for his
father to come home from work.

"Dad, can you make it rain?"
asked Rod.

Dad shook his head. "No, Rod,
I can't make it rain."

"A weatherman isn't much help,"
Rod said. "Why be a weatherman if you
can't make it rain?"

"I can tell people when a storm
is coming," said Dad. "Then they won't
get hurt. But I can't stop
the storm."

"What else can you do?" asked Rod.

"I can tell farmers when there will be
bad weather," said Dad. "And I let
the airport know when a storm is coming."

"That's a big help," Rod said. "But
I still want rain for my birthday.
Then I could have all my friends
come splash in the street."

His dad smiled and shook his head.

Dad sat down in the big chair with
his newspaper. Rod started to walk away.

"Rod," Dad called. "I'll talk to
the mayor and see what we can do."

"Thanks, Dad," said Rod. "If the mayor
has a machine to make it rain, please
talk to the mayor!"

Later that night Mother asked Dad, "Why did you let Rod think the mayor could make it rain?"

"You know it has been very dry and we need rain," said Dad.

Mother nodded. "I know," she said.

"Maybe the mayor and I can make it rain on Rod's birthday," said Dad. "We are going to try."

"Well, I would not joke that way," said Mother.

On Rod's birthday there were
many clouds, but it was hot and dry.

"Come outdoors, Rod," called Dad.
"I want to show you something."

Dad pointed to something high in the
sky. There Rod could see a plane going
back and forth, back and forth.

"Some men are putting dry ice in the
clouds," Dad said. "That is called cloud
seeding. We're trying to make it rain.
But the cloud seeding may not work."

"Thanks, Dad!" cried Rod. "I didn't
know a plane could be a weather machine."

"Oh!" Mother said. "Now I see what
you had in mind. It's not a joke at all."

Rod kept watching the sky. Would
putting dry ice in the clouds work?
He smiled when he saw the clouds turn
black. Soon it rained a little,
then a little more. Rod laughed when
the rain began splashing everywhere.

Rod ran out to the street. Soon
his friends were there, too. They
were running back and forth, splashing
water all around. How nice it felt!

"It's a happy birthday," Rod said.
"Hot days and nights will be gone.
I'm glad my dad is a weatherman!"

cheep   those   skate   wide   cube

drive   laundry   dream   drops

sent   stuck   bath   fill

anthill   chatter   sniff   bottle

Make Your Own Cloud

We see some clouds high in the sky.
Other clouds are near the ground.

If you fly into a cloud in the sky,
it is like going into fog on the ground.
A cloud is very much like fog.

What makes a cloud? Would you like
to find out?

Here is a plan for making a cloud
inside a bottle.

What You Will Need

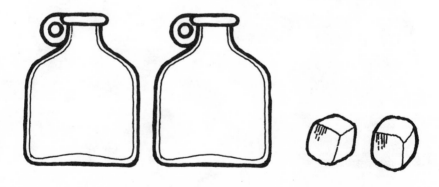

two bottles   two ice cubes

What You Do

1. Fill one bottle with hot water.
   Fill one bottle with cold water.

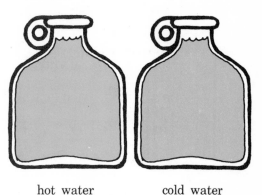

hot water   cold water

2. Take most of the water out of both bottles.
   But leave a little water in each bottle.

hot water   cold water

3. Put the ice cubes at the top of the bottles. Don't drop the ice cubes into the bottles.

hot water   cold water

Wait and see what will happen!

What Will Happen

In the bottle with hot water, the air is warm. And warm air can hold more water than cold air. The ice will make the warm air cold. As the warm air gets cold, tiny drops of water can be seen. These tiny drops of water make a cloud.

ice cube

hot water

Both clouds and fog are made of tiny drops of water. When we see clouds, we know this means the air is holding as many tiny drops of water as it can.

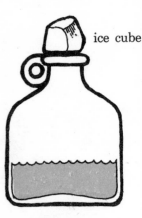

ice cube

cold water

In the other bottle, the water and the air are cold. And there is no cloud. Do you know why?

Think about This:

Can you find other ways to make clouds?

94

station mention vacation

cost clock washcloth

knocked knee gnawed

footsteps stacked almost

policemen gasoline magazines

sway saying tray

hose drive cage

construction

strong

knocking

stood

machines

Jay

crane

Sight word.

sign

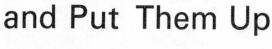

Knock
Them
Down

and Put Them Up

95

Mike and Jay were walking to school
one day when they saw something. It was
a tall, yellow, steel machine. It stood
right by an old house.

"What is that big machine?" Jay asked.
"And what's it doing by that old house?"

"I don't know," Mike said.

Just then a steel rope came down from
the machine. Some men were putting a
big steel ball on the end of the rope.

"Look," Mike said. "What are they
doing with that big ball?"

"Don't ask me," Jay said. "Let's ask
one of the workers."

"What are you doing?" Mike called to
one of the men.

"We're putting a ball on this crane,"
the man said.

"What's it for?" asked Jay.

But the man had gone back to work.

"Do you boys come by this fence every
day?" someone asked. The boys looked up.
There stood Miss Gold, their teacher.

"Yes," said both boys.

"After school you may watch to
see what the crane does," said Miss Gold.
"But now we must go to school."

After school the boys found the big crane still at work. It was picking up the steel ball and knocking it into the side of the old house.

"I still don't know what that is, but I know what it can do," said Mike. "It can knock down a house in a hurry! What a strong machine! Let's call the machine Knock-Them-Down."

"Let's ask Miss Gold if we can make a machine like that at school," said Jay. On the way home they made plans for building the crane.

At school the next day, Jay told about the machine. Then some of the children found books about machines. Mike had his construction set. Jay helped him set up the crane. It had a rope with a ball at the end. Then they put a sign by the crane.

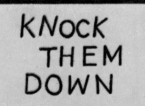

KNOCK
THEM
DOWN

The next morning the boys were on
their way to school. "Let's stop and
watch old Knock-Them-Down," Mike said.

The boys put down their books and ran
to the fence. But the strong crane
was not knocking down the house now.
It was picking up a steel beam. Then
the crane put the beam in a new place
on the ground.

"Why, old Knock-Them-Down isn't
knocking down today!" Jay cried. "It's
helping the men set up a new building.
The big ball isn't on the rope."

"What a machine!" Mike said. "We'll have to give it a new name. Some day I'm going to run a machine like that."

"Me, too!" said Jay. "I'll knock down an old building, and you can put up a new one. We'll have fun!"

After school Mike and Jay made another machine. Miss Gold laughed when she saw the new sign they put by their machines.

loose   base   geese

strings   wing   kingdom   hang

quacking   quickly   quail

banish   brushing   shout   shines

great   greens   growing   grew

among   banana   camera   parade

drew   threw   chew   grew   brew

wind   engine

lighthouse

clang

quitter

should

grin

Ida

Lewis

Ida Lewis

Mr. Lewis came home one day looking
very happy. He had a big surprise for
his family. "We are going to move to a
lighthouse," he said. "And I am going to
be the new lighthouse keeper." It would be
a new way of living for the family.

"What will you do?" Ida asked. She was
the biggest of his four children.

Mr. Lewis said, "My main work will be
to help people in boats. I will keep
the light shining in the lighthouse.
Then boats can stay away from the rocks."

"Can we help?" Ida asked.

"Maybe so," Mr. Lewis said. "There are
times when we must help each other."

Soon after their move, Ida's father
got so sick he could not work. Three of
the children were still very small, and
Mrs. Lewis had to look after them. She
wanted to leave the lighthouse and go
back to the city.

But Ida did not want to quit. "We
should give it a try," she said to her
mother. "I am strong. I can help."

Mrs. Lewis shook her head. "There will
be much to do," she said. Then she said
with a grin, "But maybe we should try."

One day while Ida was watching the sea, the wind began to blow. Soon a storm came up. Above the sound of the wind, Ida heard a voice. "Help! Help!" it cried.

"A boat must have turned over," Ida said. Her boat was at the dock. She ran to her boat and was soon racing through the water.

Ida could hear the roar of the wind. She could not even see the dock. But still she went on. "Hold on! I'm coming!" she cried.

She had to pull four men into her boat. She was wet all over. Even her hands hurt as she worked back to the dock. But at last she got them back.

This was the first time Ida helped people who had bad luck at sea.

Some time later the wind began to blow again, and the sun did not shine. Ida knew a storm was coming. But she had caught a cold and had been in bed for two days. Now she sat by the fire to keep warm.

All at once Ida heard a clang above the wind. She hurried to the window. Again she heard the clang.

"It must be a steamboat with a bell. Their engine must have quit. They need help!" she said. She picked up her coat and ran to the door.

"Ida!" her mother cried. "Stop! You can't go out in this storm. Even well people don't go out in this kind of weather."

"There are people out there who need help. I'm not a quitter! We should think of them now."

Ida was very sick. But she was not a
quitter. "I can do it," she kept saying.
She hurried to her boat and pushed off
from the dock.

The storm blew at her boat. And the
wind was wet and cold. But at last she
saw two people in the water.

Slowly, slowly she got them into her
boat. Then she started back. But the
trip back was more work. No one could
help her. She must do it alone. Now
she had two more people in the boat.
She was cold, and she hurt all over.

But she did not give up. She did bring
the people in.

By 1869 many people had heard the news
about Ida. To thank her for her help, they
gave her a new boat.

"Thank you for the boat," Ida said.
"Maybe I can help even more with it."
Then she ended by saying, "I just did what
I had to do. That's all there was to it."

Off and Away

Little piece of paper on the ground.

Going nowhere.

Doing nothing.

Flat.

Little puff of wind.

```
                                              oop
                                           oo
                                         oo
                                       oo
                                      o
                                    oo
                                 oooo
                              ooo
                           o
                         o
              ooooooooooo
                   oo
                 oo
              oooooo
           ooo
         o
```

Sw

by Robert Froman

stack   stuck   wrecker   quick

brushing   bright   bracelet

page   judge   badge   age

chalk   ouch   charm

flashing   flip   flag

crouched   creature   crew

parakeet   Costa   care   library

stacked

brother

cage

chatter

flower

Cristy

Anna

Ling

Take Care of Cristy

109

Anna's friend Homer was going
on a trip. He asked Anna to take
care of his bird, Cristy.

"Just give him birdseed and water
and keep his cage clean," Homer said.

Cristy was a little green parakeet
with a shiny yellow head. The first day
Anna gave him birdseed and some water.
He ate the seeds. Then he chattered
and flew around the living room.

The next day Cristy sat on Anna's
hand, but he didn't eat many seeds.

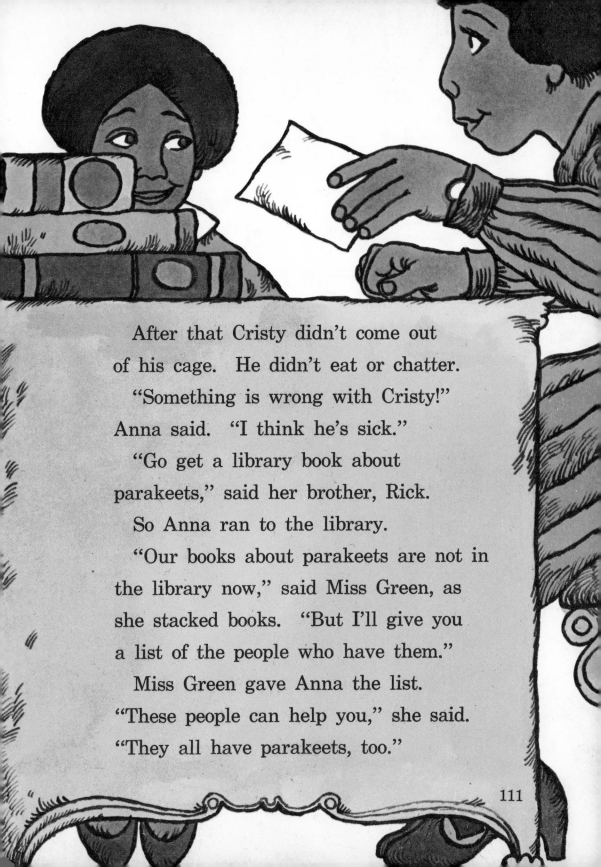

After that Cristy didn't come out
of his cage. He didn't eat or chatter.

"Something is wrong with Cristy!"
Anna said. "I think he's sick."

"Go get a library book about
parakeets," said her brother, Rick.

So Anna ran to the library.

"Our books about parakeets are not in
the library now," said Miss Green, as
she stacked books. "But I'll give you
a list of the people who have them."

Miss Green gave Anna the list.
"These people can help you," she said.
"They all have parakeets, too."

First on the list was Mr. Costa, who ran a food store. Anna went to see Mr. Costa at his store. Mr. Costa was stacking cans when Anna asked him about a parakeet book.

"My wife has the book," said Mr. Costa, as he put down the cans. "But let's see if I can help you. Did you give Cristy the same kind of seeds he had before?"

"No, I didn't," said Anna. "Should I do that?"

"Yes," said Mr. Costa. "Birds like the same kind of seeds every day. I'll give you a box of seeds for Cristy."

Anna hurried home with Cristy's seeds. He ate them at once. But he stayed in his cage, and he didn't chatter.

"Something is still wrong," Anna thought. "Cristy must be sick."

Anna looked at her list again. "I'll go ask Miss Woods if she has a parakeet book at the flower shop," she said.

"I left the book at home," said Miss Woods. "You should give parakeets some greens each day. I have some here. See if these greens will help Cristy."

So Anna gave Cristy the greens. He
left his cage to eat the wet leaves.
But he didn't chatter.

"Cristy must be sick," cried Anna.
"Mr. Ling is next on my list. I'll go
to the cleaners for his library book."

Mr. Ling worked at the cleaners down
the street. He was putting up a clean
coat when Anna asked about the book.

"I let my sister have the book,"
said Mr. Ling. "Are you sure your
bird is sick? Maybe you leave him
alone too much. You must talk to him
each day. This makes him feel better,
and he will learn to say new things."

Anna hurried home and called,
"Cristy! Pretty Cristy!"

Cristy left his cage and flew
to Anna's hand. He sat very still
and turned his head from side to side.

Anna said, "Pretty Cristy." She said
it over and over.

Cristy made a little sound and turned
around on Anna's hand. Then he
chattered and chattered to Anna.

Just then Anna's brother came in
holding three books.

"One of the parakeet books you wanted
was back in the library," said Rick.
"Then Miss Woods asked me to bring you
this book from her flower shop.
And Mr. Ling gave me a book, too.
You should know what's wrong with Cristy
after you look at all of these books!"

Rick stacked the books on the table.

Cristy flew over to Rick and sat
on the books. "Pretty Cristy!
Pretty Cristy!" chattered the bird.

"How did you teach him that?" asked
Rick. "Did you learn how from a book?"

Anna laughed. "I found out
by looking for a book!" she said.

Then Anna told Rick about Mr. Costa
and Miss Woods and Mr. Ling. She
told him how they had helped her learn
how to take care of Cristy.

Think about This:

What three things did Anna learn about
parakeets?
How else could Anna have found out more
about parakeets?

116

wreck   write   wrap

writing

squeak   squawk   squeeze

squeaky

stove   teeth   wake

waited

steady   stores   stuck   stories

stopping

spinning   spent   wasp   spoke

speak

nation   direction   invention

station

ting-a-ling

Spanish

English   Cruz   *Amigo*   Rosa

Rosa

Rosa was a small girl in a big city. Her family had just moved to the city, and Rosa didn't speak English. Each day she went for a walk with her brother and sister. But Rosa had never gone away from home alone.

Today Rosa felt very big. It was her birthday! She opened her presents first thing that morning. She liked the charm bracelet and the new shoes best of all.

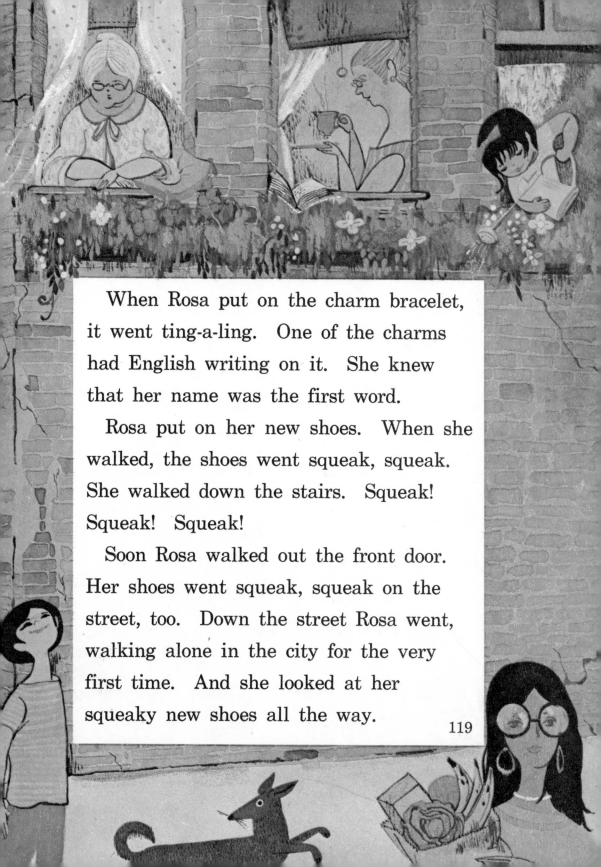

When Rosa put on the charm bracelet, it went ting-a-ling. One of the charms had English writing on it. She knew that her name was the first word.

Rosa put on her new shoes. When she walked, the shoes went squeak, squeak. She walked down the stairs. Squeak! Squeak! Squeak!

Soon Rosa walked out the front door. Her shoes went squeak, squeak on the street, too. Down the street Rosa went, walking alone in the city for the very first time. And she looked at her squeaky new shoes all the way.

119

A tall policeman was at the corner.
His long arms were stretched out,
stopping cars. He smiled kindly as
Rosa walked by. Squeak! Squeak!
Squeak! Rosa smiled at him, too.

On Rosa walked, still looking at
her shoes. Then at last she looked up.
There were strangers all around.

"I'll look for the policeman I liked,"
she thought. "He was near my house."

Rosa turned around and ran back.
She saw a policeman, but he wasn't the
one she had seen before. She wasn't
even at the same corner. So Rosa walked
on. Squeak! Squeak! Squeak!

Rosa was lost, and she was tired, too.
She sat down by a sign to rest. Before
long a policeman came by. He had seen
Rosa sitting alone.

"Are you lost?" the policeman asked.

Rosa didn't know what he was saying.
She smiled and nodded her head.

"What is your name?" he asked.

"*Amigo!*" said Rosa, and she began
to speak to him in Spanish.

"Take my hand," said the policeman.
He held out his hand to her and led the
way to the police station. "We'll go
see Mr. Cruz. He can talk to you in
Spanish and find out where you live."

But Mr. Cruz was not at the station.
So Rosa sat down and waited. Again and
again she tried to tell the policeman
where she lived. But he didn't know
what she was saying.

Rosa waited in a big room where many
strangers moved back and forth.
She didn't want to cry. So she looked
at her new shoes and played with her
charm bracelet. She turned it around on
her arm. Ting-a-ling went the charms!

A tall policeman came to the door.
Rosa had seen him that morning. He had
smiled at her.

Rosa walked up to the tall policeman.
Squeak! Squeak! went her shoes.

"You must be the little girl on First
Street with the squeaky shoes!" the
policeman said. "Come with me."

Rosa went with the policeman.
"*Amigo!*" she said, as she held up her
bracelet. Ting-a-ling! He nodded,
and then he looked at Rosa's bracelet.

"Rosa!" cried the policeman. "The
writing on your charm bracelet
tells me just where you live!"

So the tall policeman took Rosa
home in his car. How happy she felt!

She ran up the steps to the door.
Ting-a-ling! Then she turned and
called, "*Amigo!*" to the policeman.

Squeak! Squeak! Rosa's new shoes
made the best sound when they went
up the steps of her house.

smallest balk hallway

chalk

crash crawl crazy

cream

afternoon footsteps postman

sidewalk

skin mask husky

skate

strings stretch struck stray

streets

subway

PLAY
STREET

City Friends

The world of the city might surprise you if you do not live there. Children in the city see one tall building after another. They play on a sidewalk or in the streets. They ride in a subway under the streets. And all around they see people, people, people!

What does the city child do? More than you might think! He plays in a park. He may ice-skate there, too.

In summer the city child can swim
in a city pool. He can take a subway
and go to ball games. Sometimes he gets
to go to camp. At camp he can learn
about birds, bugs, and animals.

Even at home the city child has fun
in the summer. He gets ice cream from
the ice-cream man. He may make a
tree house, but it won't be in a tree.
The tree house will be on top of an old
car! And the city child can skate on
the sidewalk. He plays chalk games
on the sidewalk, too.

See if you can find a chalk picture
and a chalk game on the sidewalk.

The city child is much like a child living in the country. He has a family, and he has friends. Sometimes he has a pet, too.

City children like to swim in a pool and eat ice cream and tell a good joke. And always, like children everywhere, they wonder about the rest of the big world around them.

Think about This:

What other "sidewalk" games could city children play?

wheel whirl whisper

whistle

drank yank junk honk

yanked

carrying terrified mirror

carried

clump fix pen

send

strut straw strap strike

strings

wrapping wrecker wrist

write

oldest strongest shortest

smallest

dragon's

quiet Pepe

climbing

Pepe's Watchdog

Many children in Pepe's school had dogs
for pets. But Pepe had the smallest
dog of all. His dog would always be
small. So Pepe called his dog Tiny.

One day Pepe got a new watch. He was
showing it to a friend on the way home
from school.

"You have a watch and a dog," said
Pepe's friend. "You're lucky!"

"I know," said Pepe. And just then he
felt something bump his leg. It was Tiny.
"Sometimes I carry him in my pocket. It's
fun to have the smallest dog."

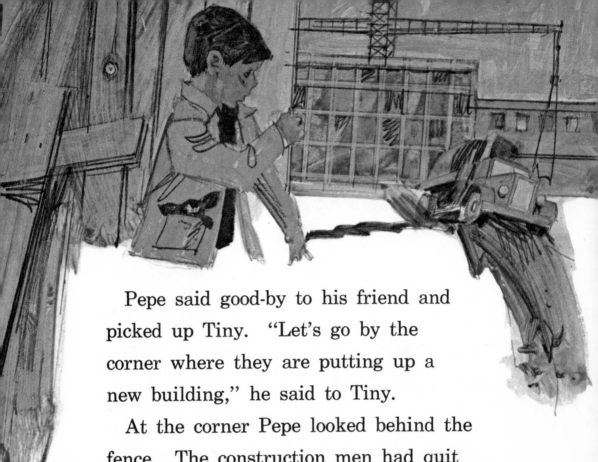

Pepe said good-by to his friend and
picked up Tiny. "Let's go by the
corner where they are putting up a
new building," he said to Tiny.

At the corner Pepe looked behind the
fence. The construction men had quit
work for the day. There was nothing in
the deep hole but dirt and a big machine.

"Let's go down there and look at
that machine," Pepe said.

Pepe put Tiny in his pocket. The dog
looked funny with just his nose and one
leg showing. Two small steps and one
long slide took them down inside the
deep hole.

"This machine looks like a dragon,"
Pepe said. "See its wide, open mouth
and pointed teeth? And it has bumpy
feet just like a dragon's."

Pepe took a stick and knocked some
dirt from the dragon's bumpy feet.

After a while Pepe looked at his watch.
He saw it was time to go. Then he looked
at the top of the hole. "How will we
ever get out of here?" Pepe thought.

He tried climbing out, but his feet
slipped on the dirt. "I always slide
back down," said Pepe. He tried
calling for help, but no one called back.

Pepe put Tiny down and walked around.
He had to find a way to send for help.
He didn't even hear a police whistle
or a car horn. It was very
quiet. It was so quiet that he knew
there were no people going by.

Pepe looked at his watch again. "It's time for dinner, and Dad is home," he thought. "I'll write a note and send Tiny home with it. Then Dad will come to help me!" Pepe looked in his pocket, but he had nothing to write on.

The side of the hole looked as high as his bedroom wall. Could Tiny climb that high? Pepe thought for a while.

All at once Pepe yanked out the strings from his shoes. He took off his watch and tied it onto Tiny with the strings. Then he carried Tiny to the side wall.

Pepe stretched and pushed until Tiny was near the top. "Go home, Tiny, go home!" he shouted. Then Pepe slipped to the ground again. "Go home, Tiny!"

Tiny climbed to the top. Then he stopped and looked back at Pepe.

"Don't just sit there, Tiny. Go home!" shouted Pepe.

Slowly Tiny got up and turned around. Then he looked back at Pepe once more.

"Go on, Tiny!" shouted Pepe. "Hurry, before it gets dark!" At last the little dog walked slowly to the sidewalk.

"Can Tiny get home?" Pepe thought. He waited and waited. He sat on the dragon's bumpy feet and tried to whistle. It was getting dark. And it was very quiet. The big machine looked more and more like a real dragon. Its teeth looked much too real!

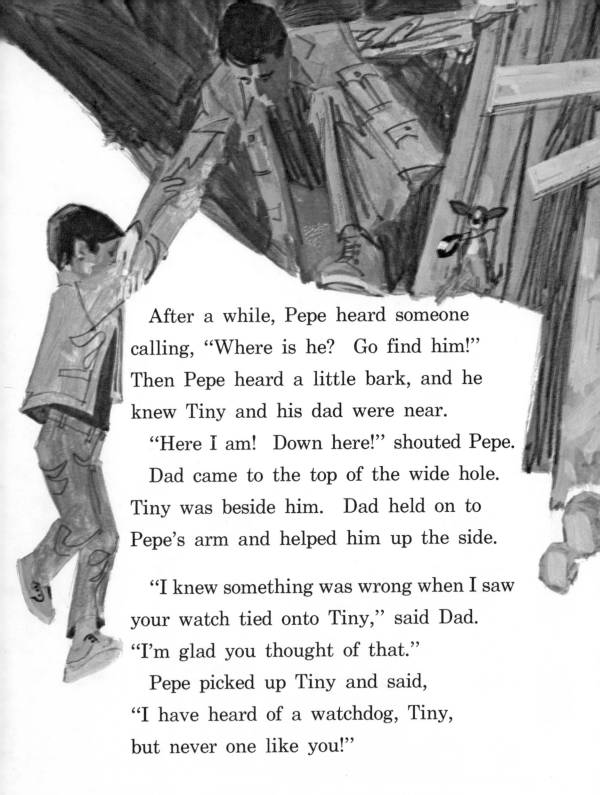

After a while, Pepe heard someone
calling, "Where is he? Go find him!"
Then Pepe heard a little bark, and he
knew Tiny and his dad were near.

"Here I am! Down here!" shouted Pepe.

Dad came to the top of the wide hole.
Tiny was beside him. Dad held on to
Pepe's arm and helped him up the side.

"I knew something was wrong when I saw
your watch tied onto Tiny," said Dad.
"I'm glad you thought of that."

Pepe picked up Tiny and said,
"I have heard of a watchdog, Tiny,
but never one like you!"

anthill   without   understand

clock   quacking   chuck

bath   thinking   third

whale   whenever   whittle

wrench   wrecks   writes

dish   shears   showed

stores   starting   steady

cheered

everyone

stuck

those

wheels

wrecker

flashing

gust

The Peanut Party

The city streets were cold. And so was Sam! His teeth began to chatter. "Let's go home, Mom," he said.

"First I'll go to the corner store," said Mom. "Then we'll catch the bus."

At the corner, a big gust of wind blew an old hat to Sam. "Look, Mom!" cried Sam as he caught the hat.

"Put it down, Sam," she said. "That old hat is no good."

"Some people like old hats," said Sam. "Dad likes his old fishing hat."

Mom laughed. "Yes, he does! Now hold my bag while I go inside the store."

While he waited, Sam watched a gust of
wind push people along. Other people
lost hats, too. Then Sam saw an old man
with a cart. The man looked at Sam.

"My hat!" the man shouted. "Where did
you find it? I have looked and looked
for it. I thank you very, very much!"

He ran back to his cart and got some
bags of warm peanuts. "I thank you 100
times," said the man. Then he put bag
after bag of peanuts into the shopping
bag Sam was holding.

Mom came out of the store and looked
around for Sam. He called to her.

The wind was blowing hard, and Sam
didn't tell his mother about the old man
until they got on the bus. "Do you know
what I'm going to do with all of those
peanuts?" said Sam. "I'm going to have
a peanut party at school!"

Just then the bus began to slide.
The snow was blowing, and it was hard to
see the street. Then the bus stopped.

"The wheels are stuck in the gutter,"
called out the driver. "We'll go again
as soon as a wrecker comes to help us."

Everyone was in a hurry to get home.
Many people were upset because the
wheels were stuck. Little children were
tired. The snow kept falling, and the
wrecker didn't come.

"I'm hungry!" cried a little boy.
And the boy's eyes were on Sam's
peanuts!

"Do you want some peanuts?" Sam asked.

"Yes!" said the boy. "I'm hungry!"

Sam gave the little boy some peanuts.
Then Sam saw the boy's mother eating
one of the peanuts. Sam looked around.
Other people were watching the little
boy eat. Sam could tell that they were
all hungry and upset, too.

"If I give my peanuts away now," Sam
thought, "I can't have a party at
school."

Sam was very quiet. It looked as if
the bus might be there a long time. It
might be more fun to have the party now.

Sam gave peanuts to everyone. Soon
they were all singing and laughing.
The singing told Sam that those peanuts
had made everyone feel better!

Sam saw the flashing light of a
wrecker in front of the bus. Then the
bus wheels began spinning and spinning.
The light kept flashing. As the bus
moved out of the gutter, everyone
cheered the wrecker. Then everyone
cheered Sam.

"Thanks for the peanut party!"
they said.

"You never know what will happen on
a bus these days!" Mom said to Sam.

able   hustle   saddle

moment   prefix   zebra

anything   clothes   thirty

understood   anywhere   himself

plate   plums   plank

thinks   thanked   bunk

really   answered

bundle

Jody

third

understand

plants

thinking

hardheaded

watermelon

policemen

The Watermelon Seeds

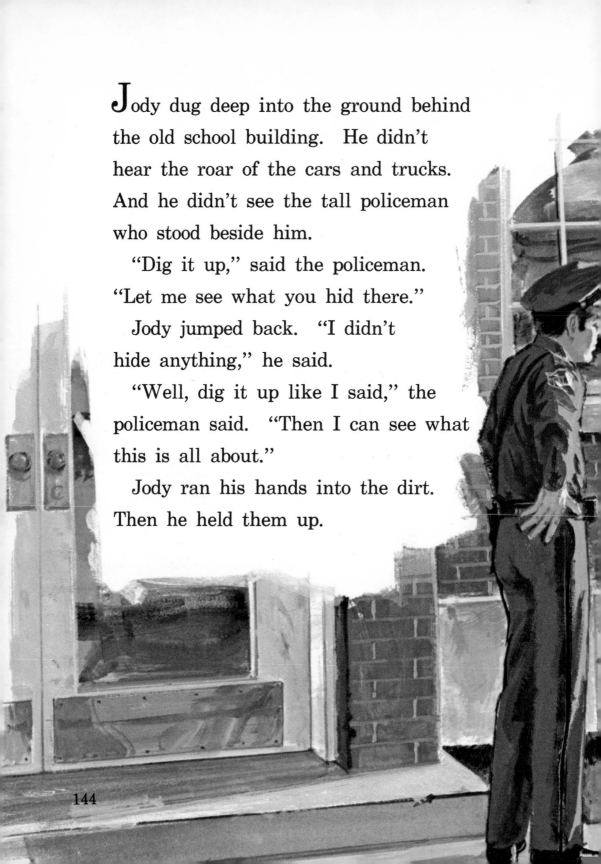

Jody dug deep into the ground behind the old school building. He didn't hear the roar of the cars and trucks. And he didn't see the tall policeman who stood beside him.

"Dig it up," said the policeman. "Let me see what you hid there."

Jody jumped back. "I didn't hide anything," he said.

"Well, dig it up like I said," the policeman said. "Then I can see what this is all about."

Jody ran his hands into the dirt. Then he held them up.

"Really, sir, there's nothing here
but watermelon seeds. See?" Jody said.

He held up some big seeds to show
the policeman. "Last night we had some
watermelon," said Jody. "I saved the
seeds. There's no place to plant them
at our apartment house across the street."

"You won't have any luck," said the
policeman. "Watermelons won't grow here."

"I'll take care of the seeds and
water them," Jody answered.

"Well, all right," said the policeman.
"Those seeds you saved won't come up.
But I guess it won't hurt anything to
plant them."

145

The days were very hot. Jody put water
on the seeds every day. But nothing
happened. Jody began thinking that
maybe the policeman was right. The
seeds might not grow.

One day Jody was working in his
garden. He didn't hear the police car stop.
"You really are hardheaded!" said a
loud voice. "I told you watermelons
won't grow in that small space!"
But the policeman grinned.
"This school is so old," said Jody.
"There's not one green thing growing
around here. I thought it would be
nice if something green was growing."
"I understand, Jody," said the
policeman. "But that ground isn't good
for growing. So don't count on any
seeds coming up." Then he drove away
in his car.

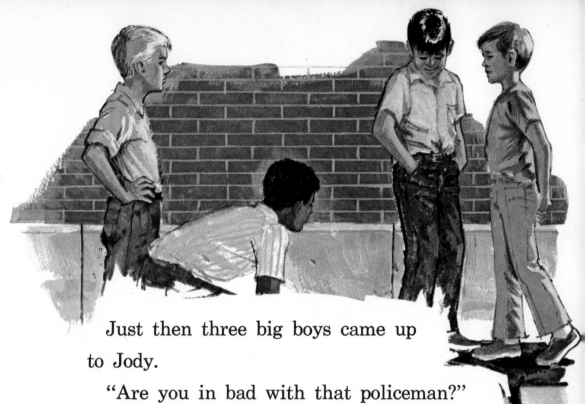

Just then three big boys came up
to Jody.

"Are you in bad with that policeman?"
one boy asked. "I saw him talking
to you. What happened?"

"Did you really take something and
hide it here?" asked another boy.

"Let's dig it up!" said the third
boy.

Jody watched the three boys dig up
his garden. They didn't understand.
Jody was all alone. What could he do?

"Nothing here!" said the third boy.
"Come on! Let's go!"

Then the three boys ran away.
Jody was so upset it was hard to put
the dirt back in place. He felt sure
that the seeds couldn't grow now. Then
he saw something that surprised him.

"This seed is growing!" he thought.
He looked for other seeds and began to
count them. He found six seeds growing!
Jody put them back into the ground and
patted the dirt around them.

In three more days there were six
plants above the ground. Jody couldn't
wait to show the policeman!

Later Jody saw the policeman. Jody called to him and pointed to the garden.

"You really are hardheaded!" said the policeman. "Do you think watermelon plants will make this school better?"

Jody looked at the old school building. "They won't make it better, I guess," said Jody. "But once I saw a school with green leaves all over it. I wish my school could look that nice."

"Jody, will you meet me here in the morning?" asked the policeman.

"Yes, sir," he answered. Then Jody walked away thinking, "Will he tell me to dig up the plants?"

The next day the policeman was
watching for Jody. In his hands
were some plants tied in a bundle.

"These plants will grow in ground next
to a building," said the policeman. "Plant
this bundle. When school starts, the
plants should be growing up the wall."

"Thank you!" cried Jody. "I didn't
know policemen were so nice!"

The policeman smiled. "We both learned
something. I learned that watermelons
will grow in a small space, and you
learned that policemen are your friends."

Then Jody and the policeman
shook hands.

bacon   dining   forever

himself   bustle   laundry

kitten   yippee   sizzle

Jeff's   Jean's   Fay's

saddle   carrying   dolls

clumping   dropped   hardest   quicker

smaller   sniff   sprig

cowboys   joined   oiled

Sight word.

phone

Sound the words.

able

empty

suddenly

Gail's

setting

oldest

smiling

voices

Ryan

The Phone Call

151

Gail was on the floor looking at a book. She turned over on her back and shut her eyes. After a while she stretched and looked in the bedroom. Beth, her little sister, was on the bed. She was smiling in her sleep. Gail couldn't help smiling with her.

"There isn't much to do," Gail said. "Maybe I'll watch TV." She turned on the TV and stretched out on the floor.

RING! went the phone. Gail jumped to her feet. "Hello," she said.

A voice was crying. "Mother is hurt."

"Where is your mother?" Gail asked.

"On the floor," the small voice said. Gail's hands shook. Suddenly she was afraid.

"What is your name?" asked Gail. There was no sound. Gail was afraid she would not be able to keep the child on the phone. "I'm the oldest one here. I must do something," she thought.

"What is your name?" she asked again.

"Ben!" he shouted. The phone was quiet. Then there was a loud clang. Ben had let the phone fall.

"Ben, come back!" Gail shouted. She heard him come back to the phone.

"Mother is hurt," he said. He was still crying.

"Ben, my name is Gail. Can you tell me where you live?"

"In a big house," he said.

"Do you know your street, Ben? Do you know its name?" Gail asked.

"My name is Ben! I told you!"

Gail knew then she would have to try something else.

Gail had to find out where Ben was.
"Ben, do you know numbers?"

"I'm four!" he shouted.

"My sister is six. I play games with
her," Gail said.

"I want to play!" Ben said.

"Good, I want to play, too," Gail said.
"But you will have to do as I say."

"I will!" Ben had stopped crying.

"Do you see the numbers on the phone?"
Gail asked.

"Yes, four—five—six and a line,"
Ben said.

"Are there any more?" Gail asked.

"Five—six—five—five," Ben said.

"That's good, Ben," said Gail. "You win.
Would you like to talk to my sister?"

"All right," Ben said.

Gail ran to the bedroom. "Get up,
Beth. Go to the phone. Your nap is
over." Beth didn't know what to
think. The kids she knew didn't call her.

"Hurry up!" Gail said. Gail was
jumping up and down. "Talk to the boy
on the phone until I get back. His name
is Ben." Beth picked up the phone,
and Gail ran out the door.

Gail looked at the house next door.
It was empty. What could she do?

"Mrs. Ryan!" Gail shouted. "Mrs. Ryan will help!" She ran across the street. Jumping up the front steps, she knocked on Mrs. Ryan's door.

"Gail, is something wrong?" Mrs. Ryan asked. Then Gail told her story. "I'll call the police! You go back to the phone."

Gail ran back home and took the phone from Beth. She put the phone to her ear and began to talk. She told Ben story after story until her voice was tired.

At last Gail heard other voices on the phone.

Then a man said, "Gail, this is Officer Kaplan. Thanks to you, Ben's mother will be all right."

"What happened to her?" Gail asked.

"She broke her foot and hurt her head. But the doctor is with her right now. Good work, Gail."

Gail put down the phone with a smile. She was the oldest, and she had done well. She felt very, very good.

Later, while Gail and Beth were setting the table, Beth was quiet for a long time. Then she said, "Gail, I'm glad you're older. I feel safe when you're around."

City

In the morning the city

Spreads its wings

Making a song

In stone that sings.

In the evening the city

Goes to bed

Hanging lights

About its head.

by Langston Hughes

ago   agree   aside

awake

terrified   happens   zebra

bacon

clumping   close   clothes

clock

gallon   sizzle   kitten

coffee

crowd   crash   crooked

crisp

saddle   kettle   noodle

hustle

stove   frown   snore

sniffs

chore   snoring   shore

stores

asleep

says

newspapers

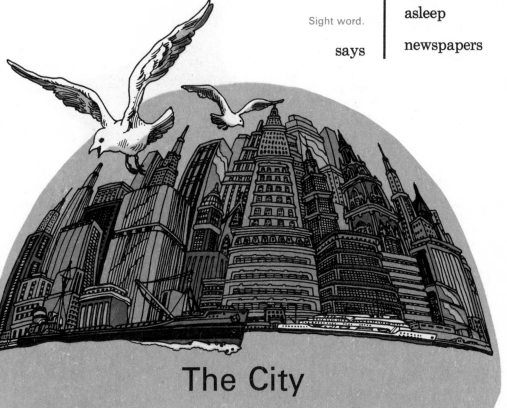

The City

Come walk with me in the city in the
morning. Here by the dock the sea air is
crisp. Look around. Men hustle and
bustle as they carry bags of coffee from
a big ship. Some of the men hum. A cat
zips by the workers and sniffs at some
dirty newspapers on the dock.

Walk on up the street with me. Now the
dock is far behind us. Here is an apartment
building. Sniff the air. There is still
the smell of the sea in the crisp morning
air. A man is cooking bacon while the
rest of the family is asleep. Look over
there. You can see him through the window.

Around the corner there are many stores.
The people who own the stores are awake
now. One woman is cleaning the sidewalk
with a hose. Next door a laundromat has
been open all night. Above the door a
sign flashes. LAUNDRY it says over
and over.

At the end of the street, there is a
firehouse. There is no need to wake the
firemen. They are all awake. Clang!
A bell rings. It must be a big fire.
The chief himself is going. Hear the
noises. Another bell clangs. The trucks
roar. Then all is quiet again.

It is later now. The clock says ten.
There is more hustle and bustle on the
city streets.

Hear the noises of the day. City
birds cheep in small voices. Cars drive
up and down. People hurry past. Some
of them hold newspapers under their
arms. Some are happy and some are sad,
but most are in a hurry.

CLANG! Two steel beams fall from a
truck. "Stop the truck!" a woman cries.
A policeman sees the beams fall and
helps the driver put them back. "Thanks!"
calls the truck driver. The policeman
hears him and walks away with a smile.

It has been a fine walk. And the day
in the city goes on.

We work with words.

cowboy showed power

fourth shouldn't ours south

almost clothes roll

wad watchman wasp

choose cause nurse

killer favor collar

dough daughter brought

Sight word.

iron

Sound the words.

frown

proud

postman

wash

close

owner

straight

Soo

Lotus

grandfather

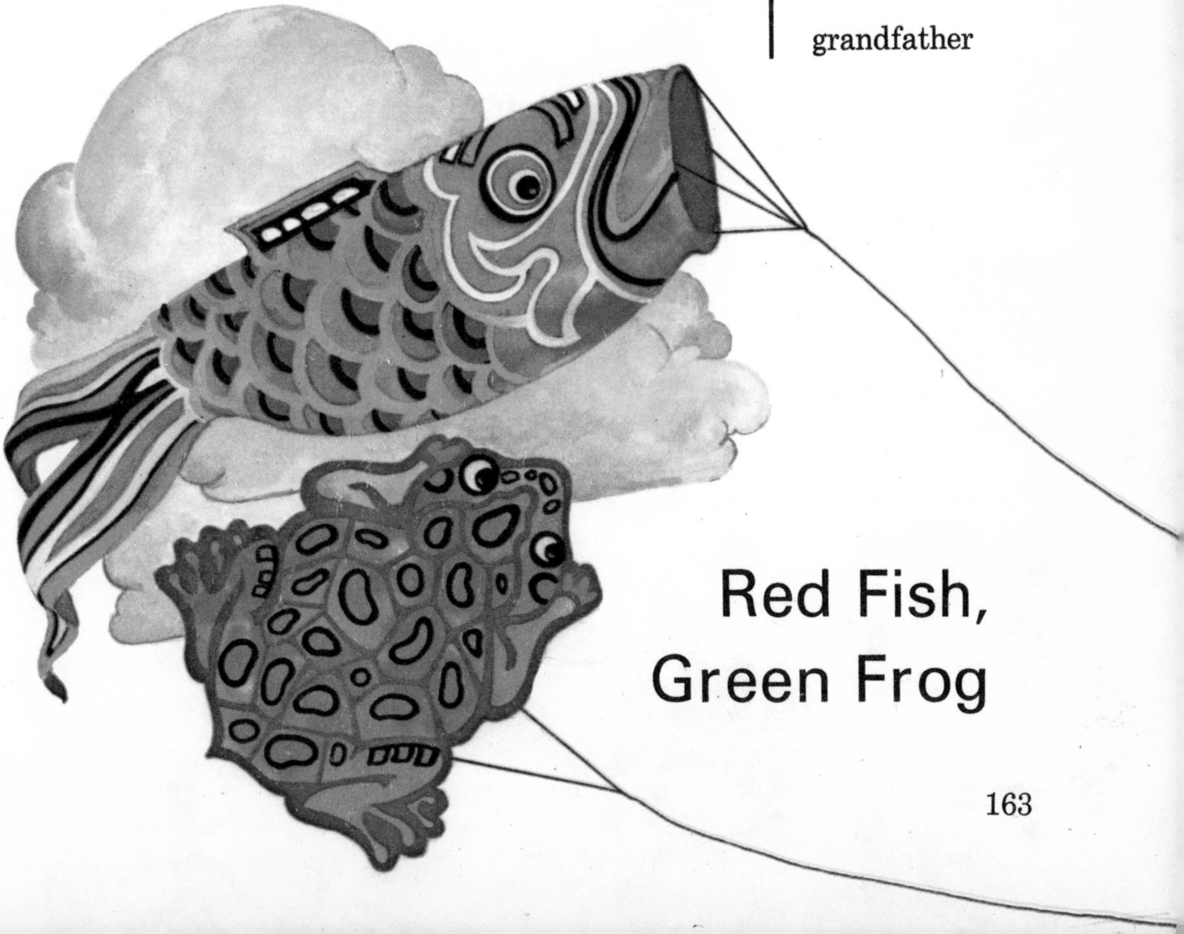

Red Fish, Green Frog

Kim ran down the street to the Lotus
Toy Shop. Through the window she could
see Mr. Soo, the owner. But of all the
toys, the one she liked best was a big
red fish kite. It was just what she
wanted to win the kite race.

Kim went inside and picked the kite
up. "How much is this kite?" she asked.

"Well," said Mr. Soo, "I can sell it
to you for two dollars."

"Oh!" said Kim. "Is it that much?"

"Yes," Mr. Soo said, "but it is the
best kite I have."

Kim took one last look at the kite.
"Two dollars," she said. "But it is the
best kite in town."

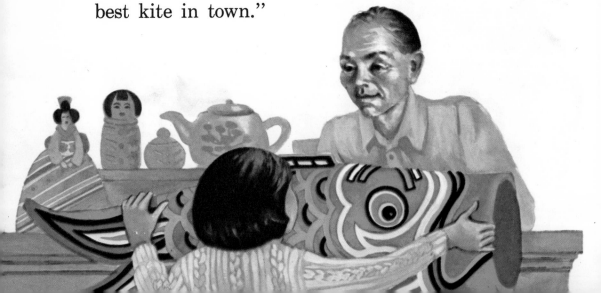

Kim left the toy shop and walked down the street with a frown on her face. She wanted to find her grandfather to tell him about the kite. On the way she met the postman, Mr. Jun. "Have you seen my grandfather?" she asked him.

"He got on a bus," Mr. Jun said.

Kim ran to the corner and climbed on the bus. She knew her grandfather would be fishing under the iron bridge.

When the bus stopped, Kim climbed off and raced to the iron bridge. "Grandfather!" she shouted. "I need two dollars."

"Don't frown, Kim. Maybe you can make two dollars," Grandfather said.

"But how?" Kim asked. She looked at the water. "How can I make two dollars?" Kim thought and thought. Then she looked at her grandfather's fishing rod. "That's it!" she cried. "I'll catch fish and sell them to Mr. Ling at the fish market."

Kim hurried to Mr. Ling's market.
"Mr. Ling," she said, "many people will
be coming to town to see the kite race."

"Yes," Mr. Ling said with a frown.
"I don't know how I'll ever get all the
fish they will need."

"I'll tell you how," Kim said. "If you
can give me two dollars, I'll bring you all
the fish you want. I'll even clean and
wash them."

"Good," said Mr. Ling. "We're partners."
Kim went fishing under the iron bridge
every day. And every day there was a smile
on her face. She went fishing before school.
She went fishing after school. "Fish,"
she said, "you are getting me my red fish
kite." And every day she carried fish to
Mr. Ling.

Then the day of the kite race came.
Kim did not think she could wait for the
race. But she took time to wash the last
of her fish and take them to Mr. Ling.
"Here, partner," she said. He gave her
the two dollars.

Kim ran straight to Mr. Soo's shop.
"My, what a big smile!" Mr. Soo said.
"Here, I saved your kite." Kim thanked
him and ran out the door into the sun.

On the way to the kite race, Kim met
the postman. "Good luck, Kim!" he cried
as she ran by.

She ran all the way to the kite race.
Some of the kites were in the air. But
soon her fish kite was up with them.
Higher and higher it climbed.

Only a green frog kite was as high as
her fish kite. Kim let out more string.
Her kite did a flip and climbed some more.
Up went the green frog kite. Again Kim
let out more string.

It was a close race. First the green
frog kite would go up. Then Kim's kite
would flip and go up.

"I don't have much string left," Kim
said. But the green frog went up again.
Kim let out the last of her string. Just
then a strong wind yanked the string
right out of her hands.

Up, up her kite floated. Soon it was
a red spot in the sky. Then it flew
straight for a tall building.

"Oh, no!" Kim cried. "It's going to hit!"

It floated very close to the building.
But it did not hit. Suddenly the end of
the long string caught on the tip of the
building.

There it flew, high above every other
kite in the world. Kim looked at her kite
high in the sky. She was so proud she
thought she would sing. The red fish kite
was the best after all.

Wings
Over
Sky
Ranch

We work with words.

mailbox	storyteller	yourself
ouch	beaches	chance
takes	sides	seem	hope
sacks	thick	ticket
wouldn't	shout	yourself

Sound the words.

cowboy

ranch

rode

chuck

without

wagon

Sight word.

changed

From Horse to Helicopter

171

A cowboy had to work hard in the Old West. On a big ranch, he might work alone for days. He might go without much food or sleep for weeks at a time.

The cowboy had to work outdoors. So he had a big hat to keep the sun and rain off his face. And he had to wear high-heeled boots to help him in his work.

A cowboy could not work without his horse. He rode for days roping cattle. He rode for weeks to get them to market.

A chuck wagon was sent with the cowboys on a cattle drive. The chuck wagon carried food for the cowboys.

Today things have changed for the cowboy. Machines help with his work. Now a cowboy may drive a jeep or even fly a helicopter. In a jeep he gets around the ranch faster than on a horse. He can round up cattle from a helicopter. Then the cattle can be sent to market by train or truck. Today a fast truck is used for a chuck wagon.

Some things have not changed for the
cowboy. He still rides a horse some
of the time. And he still must
work out in the sun and rain.
So he wears a big hat just like the
old-time cowboys. He wears
high-heeled boots, too. Roping cattle
is part of his work even today.

A cowboy on a ranch still works
very hard. But the jeep, the truck,
and the helicopter have changed his
way of working.

The cowboy has come a long way
from horse to helicopter.

prey　whey

hey

paws　haul　crawl　sauce

awful

toss　happening　stiff

Jeff

afternoon　remember　mistake

sisters

pay　spray　swaying

Slay

pencil　juicy　center

Cindy

piece　priest　shield

field

retire　hired　admire

fires

Sight word.

Miguel

Little Jeff

Jeff sat at the round table with his family. Cindy and Jean, his sisters, were talking about making a birthday cake for him. Today was the big day!

But Jeff was thinking about the two things he wanted for his birthday. The first was a ride in Uncle Bill's plane. Uncle Bill was flying to Sky Ranch today. So Jeff might get his ride.

What Jeff wanted most was for Dad to stop calling him Little Jeff. But Dad had always called him that, and Jeff was afraid he always would.

"Looks as if a bad storm is coming, Little Jeff," said Dad suddenly. Jeff looked up with a frown. But he didn't say anything.

"Will Uncle Bill come?" asked Jean.

"Bill won't miss coming to the ranch if he can help it," said Dad. "Well, there's work to do. Put on your coat, Little Jeff, and meet me at the barn."

So Jeff met Dad at the barn. They took hay to the cows in the back pasture. Then Miguel, who worked for Dad, came out with some hot lunch.

"Looks as if the storm is coming soon," said Dad as they started to eat.

"There's Mr. Slay," called Jeff,
as a car drove up to the gate.

"Some of your cows are out," Mr. Slay
called. "I'll help you round them up!"

Dad looked at the sky. "Thanks,
Mr. Slay," he said. "Let's go!"

Jeff ran up to Dad. "May I help,
Dad?" he asked.

"There's something else I want you
to do, Little Jeff," said Dad. "I'm
going to let you bring your Uncle Bill
down on the landing field. It's going
to get dark soon. So go to the landing
field when it's time for the plane. The
lights must be turned on so Uncle Bill
can see to land. Will you do that?"

"Yes, Dad. I will!" answered Jeff.

Jeff ran to the house and turned on
the TV. He wanted to see if he could
hear anything about the storm. But the
TV didn't work. Then Jeff tried to turn
on the lights, but nothing happened.

"Hey, Miguel!" said Jeff. "Do you know
what this means? The lights are off.
So the lights won't turn on at the
landing field. How can Uncle Bill see
to land without lights? This is awful!"

Miguel didn't say anything, but Jeff
could tell that he was upset.

"I know what we can do!" Jeff said. "We can light big fires at each end of the landing field and along each side."

"Good thinking!" said Miguel. "But we must go to the field and work fast."

Together they picked up wood for the fires. Then they got each pile ready to light. "We'll light the fires when we hear the plane," said Jeff.

"I'll run like the wind to light them, Little Jeff," said Miguel.

Time went slowly. But at last they heard a faraway sound. Jeff and Miguel ran around starting the fires. One after another the fires caught.

"What if that sound isn't really Uncle Bill's plane?" thought Jeff. "The fires will all burn out. Then there won't be anything left to burn when Uncle Bill does come. That would be awful!"

Jeff was upset, but he kept on working with the fires. Soon the faraway sound turned into a roar. Was the roar too loud to be Uncle Bill's plane? Could it be another plane flying low because of the bad weather? Jeff looked up.

"Hey, we did it!" Jeff shouted. "It's Uncle Bill's plane coming in!"

"Yes, we did it!" shouted Miguel.

About that time Dad drove up. Uncle Bill was landing. Everyone began talking at once.

"Our Little Jeff saved the day,"
Miguel told Dad. "I think from now on
we should call him Big Jeff."

"I'm proud of you, Jeff!" said Dad.
"Let's drop Little and just say Jeff."

"When the storm is over," said Uncle
Bill, "I'll take Jeff up in my plane."

"Thanks, Uncle Bill!" said Jeff.

"Let's have some of the birthday cake
your sisters made," said Dad. "Jean and
Cindy might have presents for Jeff, too."

Jeff laughed to himself. "Dad would be
surprised if he knew I have my two
best birthday presents right now!"

brook   choose   understood

steady   heals   break

alley   honey   turkey

cost   counted   corn

sandal   happens   kir.gdom

tumble   sizzling   puddle

kettle   jolly   terrified

afternoon

great

donkey

Cactus

parade

saddle

yippee

jeans

worn

lead

A Saddle for Cactus

Cactus was the only burro on Sky Ranch.
Cactus had long ears and a funny tail
like a donkey. He showed his teeth when
he was happy. Cindy liked him more than
all of her dolls put together.

Cindy rode Cactus every day. In the
morning she would put on her blue jeans
and red shirt. Then she would put the
little brown saddle on Cactus. And off
they would start!

"Let's go out to Beaver Hill this
morning, Cactus," Cindy would say. "Or
would you like to go splash in the pond?"

"Hee-haw!" answered Cactus.

Before long Cindy's blue jeans and shirt were looking old. And the little brown saddle was just about worn out.

One day Dad said, "Our town is going to have a big parade. The mayor wants you and Cactus to lead the parade, Cindy."

"Yippee!" shouted Cindy. "I'm going to start getting Cactus ready right now. My little burro must look as great as a big horse. I'll fix his saddle. Mother, will you fix the hole in my jeans?"

"I think you need some new jeans if you're going to lead the parade," said Mother.

"Let's go into town and get a new saddle for Cactus," said Dad.

"Great!" shouted Cindy, and she ran to tell Jeff and Jean about the parade.

Cindy spent every afternoon that week brushing Cactus and showing him how to walk in a parade.

The afternoon of the parade, Cindy put
on her new jeans and shirt.

"Ouch!" she cried. "Something is in
my shirt!"

Mother looked inside Cindy's shirt.
"You forgot to take off the price
tag," said Mother. "The pins are next
to your neck. I'll get them out."

"That's better," Cindy said, as she
rubbed her neck.

Now it was time to get Cactus ready.
Cindy gave him one more brushing. Then
Dad helped Cindy put the new saddle on
Cactus. Suddenly Cactus made an awful
noise! His ears went back. He put his
head down and kicked both back feet.

"It must be the new saddle," said Dad.
"It may be too small. I'll take it off."

"What about the parade?" asked Cindy.

"Can he wear his old saddle?"
Mother asked.

"The old saddle is too worn for
the parade," said Dad. "And I can't
let Cindy ride without a saddle."

Cindy was upset. She rubbed her eyes
to keep from crying. Then she rubbed
her neck, which still hurt a little.

"Dad!" called Cindy. "Did we take the price tag off the new saddle?"

Her dad looked around the side of the saddle. Then he felt under the saddle. "Ouch!" cried Dad. There was the price tag! He yanked it off.

"That's why Cactus kicked like a donkey!" said Cindy. "Yippee! Let's go!"

They were all laughing as they put the new saddle on the little burro.

Cindy and Cactus led the parade. Cactus showed all his teeth as he walked by the mayor. "Hee-haw!" said Cactus.

Everyone laughed, the mayor most of all.

beauty

beautiful

full   bush   pulling

bushy

card   parts   smart

yard

guard   guest   guessing

guide

wool   footsteps   foods

brook

ranch's   charming   crouch

Duchess

pedal   mistake   narrator

remember

anywhere   forever   washcloth

understood

crouched

Duchess

One day Dad called from the door,
"Jean, I have a surprise for you!"

"I'm coming, Dad," said Jean. She
went into the living room.

"A dog!" Jean cried, as she ran
across the room.

"I have found a fine new friend for
you, and her name is Duchess," said Dad.

The big yellow and white dog wagged
her bushy tail and walked closer to Jean.
"Oh, she is beautiful, Dad!" said Jean.
"I'll take good care of her. I have
wanted a dog for the longest time."

"We didn't have a dog before," said
Dad, "because of Jeff's sheep. So if
Duchess can't get along with the sheep,
we can't have her at the ranch."

"I won't let her go near Jeff's
sheep," said Jean.

She showed Duchess the house and
the yard and the barn. Then she took
her down to the pasture gate.

Jean patted the gate and said, "No, no,"
to Duchess. Duchess barked and wagged
her tail. Jean thought Duchess understood.

After that, Duchess ran in the woods and
the fields. But she seemed to remember
to stay away from the sheep pasture.

"I'm sure she will remember," said Jean.

One day when it was raining, all the
family went to town. Duchess started
to go to sleep in the barn. Then she
heard a new sound. It was the cry of
a sheep.

Duchess pushed open the barn door with
her paws. She ran around the yard and
jumped over the pasture gate. The sound
was coming from the end of the pasture.

Duchess came to a brook. The cry was
closer now. She ran by the brook until
she came to a rock pile. There was a
little lamb, crouched under a rock.
His legs were caught, and he couldn't
move.

Duchess seemed to know what to do.
She moved the rock away with her paws.
Then the little lamb could get free.

Now other sheep were coming to the
brook. It was still raining, and the
water was getting high. Duchess seemed
to know that she must keep the sheep
away from high water.

She climbed to the top of a rock and
barked. The sheep ran close together.
Then Duchess got behind them and barked.
It seemed that the sheep understood.
They ran up the hill. Duchess ran
along to guide them. Then she heard
someone calling. It was Jean. She
was on the hill with her family.

"Duchess! What are you doing in the
sheep pasture?" cried Jean.

Duchess was so afraid that she put
down her head and bushy tail. Then she
crouched close to the wet ground.

Then Jeff saw the high water.

"Bring the sheep on up the hill, Duchess! Bring them all the way!" Jeff called. "You have saved my sheep!"

Duchess barked to guide the sheep, and slowly they came up to the gate.

"Beautiful Duchess, you saved the sheep!" said Jean. "Jeff, can't Duchess take care of them from now on?"

"That's fine with me!" said Jeff.

Think about This:

What is another good name for this story?

In what other ways could Duchess help at the ranch?

corn	order	lord	ordered
workmen	words	worm	worry
airline	haircut	fairy	pair
anthill	mailbox	popcorn	anywhere
quacked	quick	quake	quickly
hardly	large	marble	smart	smartest
dead	heavy	heads	mean	steady
love	second	honey	none	loves

The Lost Sheep

195

After Duchess saved the sheep, she
took good care of them. She watched
them all day long. She drove them
home every night. Even Jeff said she
was the smartest sheep dog anywhere.

But one day Duchess was late. Jeff
began to worry about the bad things that
might happen to his sheep.

"Let's go to the sheep pen," Jeff said
to his sisters. "Duchess is late, so
something must be wrong. Maybe she
isn't taking care of the sheep any more."

"Duchess will remember to bring them
home," said Cindy as they walked to the
pen. "She loves your sheep."

"Look! Here comes Duchess with the
sheep right now," said Jean.

"But something is wrong," Cindy said.

"Yes, Duchess is making the sheep run
like she did near the high water,"
Jean said. "But there isn't any
high water now."

"Stop, Duchess!" ordered Jeff. Then
he said, "Jean, she can't take care of
the sheep if she runs them."

"Something is wrong if she runs them,"
Jean said. "Are the sheep all there?"

Jeff counted quickly. Then he counted
again. "Three sheep are gone!" he cried.

Duchess drove the sheep into the pen.
Then she came over to Jean. She
barked, wagged her bushy tail, and
started back to the pasture.

"Duchess is trying to get us to go
with her," Cindy said.

"Let's go, then," said Jeff. He took
a few steps and stopped.

"We should tell Mother and Dad that
we're going," he said. "They might
worry."

"I'll go tell them," Cindy said.
"Then Dad and I can follow you on the
horse."

"Good," Jeff said. "Let's go, Jean."

Duchess led them far out in the
pasture. On and on they went into
the ranch's high hills. Then Duchess
stopped. She barked again and again.

"What is it now?" Jeff asked. "Come
on, Duchess! We must find the sheep."

"Wait!" said Jean. "Duchess is smart. We should see what she wants." So they went up a hill after Duchess. Then they heard a sheep. It seemed far away.

"Look! There's your sheep," Jean said. Then they heard some little sounds.

"And that's the baby lambs," Jeff said. "But where are they?"

"Duchess knows," Jean said. "Let's hurry."

They ran quickly to the dog. She stood by a deep hole in the ground. Down in the big hole was a pair of lambs. They couldn't get out.

"I didn't know that hole was here," Jean said.

"Look, Jean, it's not just a hole— it's a cave!" cried Jeff. "How can we get the lambs out?"

"We'll have to get Dad," said Jean. "If you go down there by yourself, you can't get out."

"I think I can," Jeff said.

"Wait! Here come Dad and Cindy now," said Jean. "You won't have to try it by yourself."

Dad rode up on the ranch's biggest roping horse. Cindy was riding behind him on the big horse.

"How can we get my lambs out, Dad?"
asked Jeff.

"I'll show you," said Dad. Then he
tied one end of a rope to his saddle.
"Steady, boy!" ordered Dad. "Steady!"
Then he dropped the other end of the
rope down into the cave.

"Hold the horse steady," Dad said.
"He knows how to keep the rope tight."

Then Dad climbed down the rope
into the cave.

Dad held up one of the lambs for Jeff to take. Next he held up the other lamb. Then Dad climbed up the rope as his horse held it tight.

"I'll get Miguel to help me look into the cave," said Dad. "It may be a big one."

Duchess started taking the sheep and the pair of lambs home.

"She is a very smart dog, isn't she?" asked Jean.

"Yes, she is," said Jeff. "I guess she really is the smartest dog anywhere. And she loves my sheep as much as I do!"

eight   weigh   sleigh   weighed

bear   nearly   early   shear

almost   post   rolled   clothes

cloth   bath   thinks   gather   gathered

jolly   thirty   sticky   heavy

booth   noodles   cook   wool

bushel   pudding   pulls   full

power

My Dad
Shears Sheep

From fall to spring you can find my father on Sky Ranch. But from spring to fall it might be hard to find him at all. He goes from ranch to ranch doing his work. My father shears sheep.

Dad has sheared sheep for a long time. At first he could shear just 25 sheep a day. But now he shears 150 in a day.

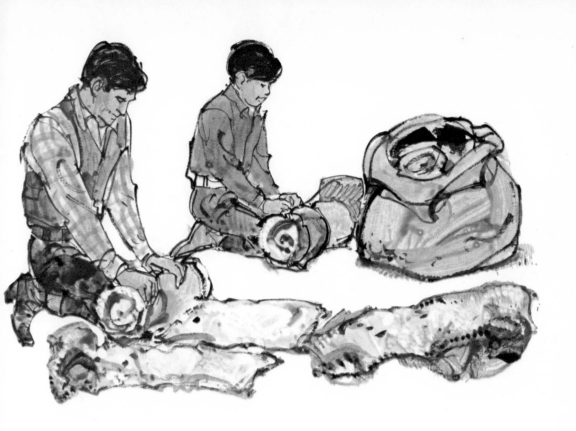

One day I went along when Dad
sheared sheep. He held each sheep
and cut off the wool with power shears.
These power shears never hurt the sheep.
As the wool fell, I gathered it and rolled
it. Then I tied it with string and put
the rolled wool into big sacks. Soon
the sacks were full and very heavy.

Dad weighed all the heavy sacks. On
each sack I wrote how much it weighed.

Soon the heavy sacks were gathered
and sent to a mill. And at the mill,
the wool will be made into clothes.
The clothes will be sent to stores. Wool
clothes are warm, and they wear well.

My father and his work help all of us.
That is why I am proud of him. Some
day I may shear sheep, too.

Think about This:

Why are sheep sheared in warm
weather?
Why does a man go from ranch
to ranch to shear sheep?

popcorn	stories	north	corn
spread	feather	heads	dead
Monday	staying	swayed	lay
raise	grease	cheese	geese
shouldn't	pound	ours	south
beat heal	sweat	mean	heals

A Wild Goose Flying

Down on Ice

Jeff and Jean knew it had turned very
cold in the night. They hurried down to
see the ice on the lake. Then Jeff saw
something white on the ice.

"Jean, come here," Jeff called to his
sister. "Look! A wild goose."

"He's not dead, is he?" asked Jean.

"No, he's not dead, but he's hurt,"
said Jeff. "He needs help. Let's
take him up to the house."

Dad looked at the goose. "That's
a snow goose," he said. "He must have
been flying south for the winter. His
wing is hurt. But after the wing
heals, he should be all right."

Miguel helped make a pen in the barn
for the goose. Cindy put hay on the
floor of the pen. Jean put a pan of
water and some corn in the pen.

After a while the goose began to eat
some corn. In a few days he was eating
all they put out for him.

"Just what do you plan to do with the goose?" Mother asked one day. "He can't sit in that pen forever."

"I guess we'll let him fly south when his wing heals," Jeff said.

Mother shook her head. "His wing may not be strong for a long time," she said. "I don't think he can fly south this winter."

"He needs to be with some other geese," said Jeff.

"Next spring he might fly with the other geese," said Mother. "But I don't know what he would do after being in a pen all winter."

"Let's keep him forever," said Jean.

"He isn't ours, you know," said Mother.

"Not ours?" asked Jean. "Why?"

"The goose is a wild animal, dear," Mother said. "And people don't own wild things."

Jeff and Jean knew that no one could
really own a wild goose. But they
didn't know how to let the goose go free.

"You can move him to the big chicken
run," said Dad. "The goose will be
safe there. But he may not be happy."

"Why won't he be happy?" asked Jeff.

Dad answered slowly. "If you had
wings that could take you up in the sky,
would you like being in a chicken pen?"

"Well, no," Jeff said. He watched as
the goose lay close to the fence.
It wanted to be free.

filled sighed cooked headed   joked

dots kills heads rises   sides

chairs pairs stairway   airline

frost toss song   cost

shouldn't she'll they're   he'll

ranger

Flying South

One day Jean found a picture of a great jet plane.   Under the picture was FLY SOUTH FOR THE WINTER!

"Fly south for the winter!" Jean thought.   "That's what our goose wants to do.   I see him beat his great wings on the sides of the pen."

Then Jean ran to see Mother.

"Mother, would a jet take our goose south for the winter?" asked Jean.

"A jet plane?" asked Mother. Then she saw the picture. "Yes, if the goose were in a crate. But I think it would cost too much money."

"Can we find out how much it would cost?" asked Jean.

"Our airport is far away," said Mother. "We can't go that far."

"I'll write to an airline," said Jean.

"I guess you could do that," said Mother. "Let Jeff help you."

So Jeff helped Jean write to an
airline. A few days later, a man came
to see them. He said, "I'm a ranger.
I have some boxes for Jeff and Jean."

"That's us!" cried Jeff.

"The airline wants to fly your goose
south—for free," said the ranger.
"These boxes are to thank you
for having saved the wild goose."

Jean opened her box. "Oh, I have a
picture of a snow goose flying high
in the sky," she said. "Now I can
remember how our snow goose looks."

"Well, I have something to help us
remember how he flew south," laughed
Jeff. He held up a toy jet plane.

The ranger went to see the goose.
He put a band around one of its legs.
Then he put the goose inside a crate,
making sure the sides were shut tight.

"Will the other geese be nice to him?"
Jean asked. "Or will they be mean?"

The ranger laughed. "Because your
goose rode in a plane?" he joked.

"No," Jean said. "They might be mean
because he didn't fly south with them."

"Your goose will be late getting
south. But the other geese will take
him in. I put the band on his leg so
we'll know if we ever see him again."

Jean looked at her picture. "Maybe
he'll fly back in the spring," she said.

"Maybe he'll remember us," said
Jeff. "We'll always remember him!"

Something Told the Wild Geese

Something told the wild geese
    It was time to go.
Though the fields lay golden
    Something whispered, "Snow."

Leaves were green and stirring,
    Berries, luster-glossed,
But beneath warm feathers
    Something cautioned, "Frost."

by Rachel Field

DUCKS, DRAGONS, AND A KING

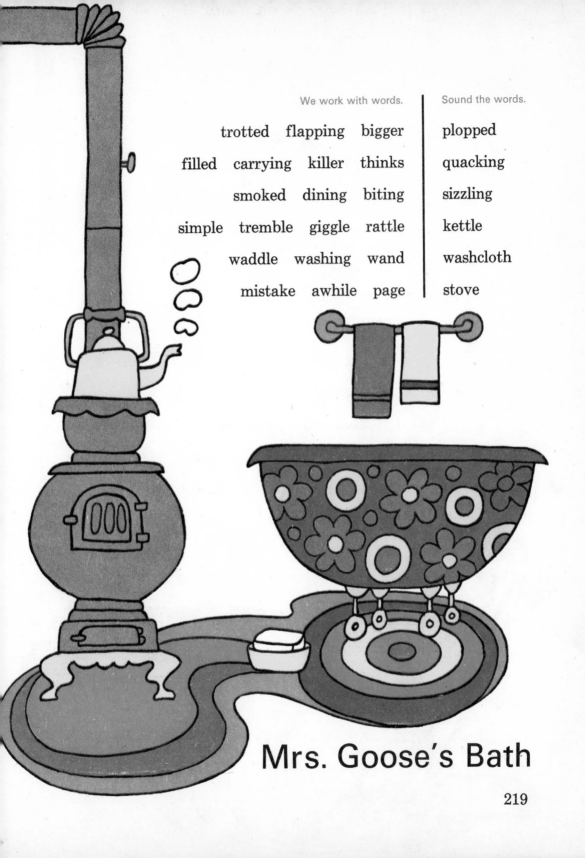

We work with words.

trotted	flapping	bigger	
filled	carrying	killer	thinks
	smoked	dining	biting
simple	tremble	giggle	rattle
	waddle	washing	wand
	mistake	awhile	page

Sound the words.

plopped

quacking

sizzling

kettle

washcloth

stove

Mrs. Goose's Bath

One day Mrs. Goose said to herself,
"I think I'll take a nice bath in my
little green tub. I don't like water
as well as my friends, Three-Ducks.
But today I'm going to take a good bath
and get all wet."

Mrs. Goose rolled out her little green
tub. She filled the kettle with water and
put it on the stove to get warm. Then
she put some soap beside the tub.

"Now I'll read my newspaper while
the water is getting warm," said
Mrs. Goose. "Then I'll start my bath."

220

After Mrs. Goose read one story, she
thought, "My water must be warm now."
So she went over to the tub.

"Oh, I forgot to get a washcloth,"
she said.

Quickly she got a blue washcloth and
put it in the tub. She picked up the
soap. Then she plopped into the tub
herself.

"The soap is here, and the washcloth
is here," she said to herself. "But this
doesn't seem like a bath."

Mrs. Goose began to rub herself
with the washcloth. "Soap, washcloth,
me. Rub, rub! Soap, washcloth, me,"
she said. "But this doesn't seem
like a bath."

Just then she heard her friends,
Three-Ducks, quacking outside. She
plopped out of the tub to see what the
quacking was all about. She pushed up
the window and stuck out her long,
funny neck.

"Three-Ducks!" she called. "Come
and tell me what isn't right about my
bath. Something is just not right."

Three-Ducks laughed. "Did you
forget the soap?" they asked.

Mrs. Goose looked around. "No,
I have it," she said.

"What about a washcloth?" asked the
ducks.

Mrs. Goose looked around again. "No,
I have it," she said. "It's a blue one,
and here it is."

"We'll come in and look," said
Three-Ducks. And they did.

There was the little green tub. There
were the washcloth, the soap, and
Mrs. Goose. And on the stove the
sizzling kettle seemed very hot.

Then the ducks looked at Mrs. Goose and began to laugh. "We knew you were funny," they said. "But we didn't know you were as funny as that!"

"Well, what about my bath?" asked Mrs. Goose.

Three-Ducks laughed so hard they could only say, "The water, Mrs. Goose, you forgot the water!"

Mrs. Goose looked at the sizzling kettle still filled with her bath water. Then she began to laugh, too. "I knew there was something I didn't have," she said. "It didn't seem like a bath!"

swaying   prayer   enjoyed   swayed

spying   frying   copying   carrying

stories   worried   dirtiest   terrified

neighbor   eighty   freight   neighbors

dining   popping   happening   clumping

hunter   softer   catcher   killer

trotted   almost   zebra   mistake

jerk   return   circus   thirty

lives   giant   George

Mr. Ant's Mistake

One morning Mr. George I. Ant moved to a new town. But no one saw him moving in. Everyone was still asleep.

It was not hard for Mr. Ant to find his new home. He had a wife and thirty children. So he moved into the biggest home on the anthill.

"First, I must paint my name on my mailbox," said Mr. Ant. "But there isn't room for all of it. I'll paint G for George and I for my middle name. And then I'll paint my last name."

That afternoon Mr. Ant went for a
walk. He was a friendly ant who wanted
to meet his neighbors. But the streets
were empty.

"Where is everyone?" Mr. Ant thought.
Then he went home and ate dinner.

The next morning Mr. Ant went walking
again. But the streets were still empty.

"What has happened?" he asked himself.

The third day Mr. Ant ran along all
the streets of the town. But not another
ant did he find. "This is awful!" he cried.

Suddenly Mr. Ant heard footsteps.
Clump, clump, clump. At first the
sound came from far away. Then the
footsteps came closer and closer.

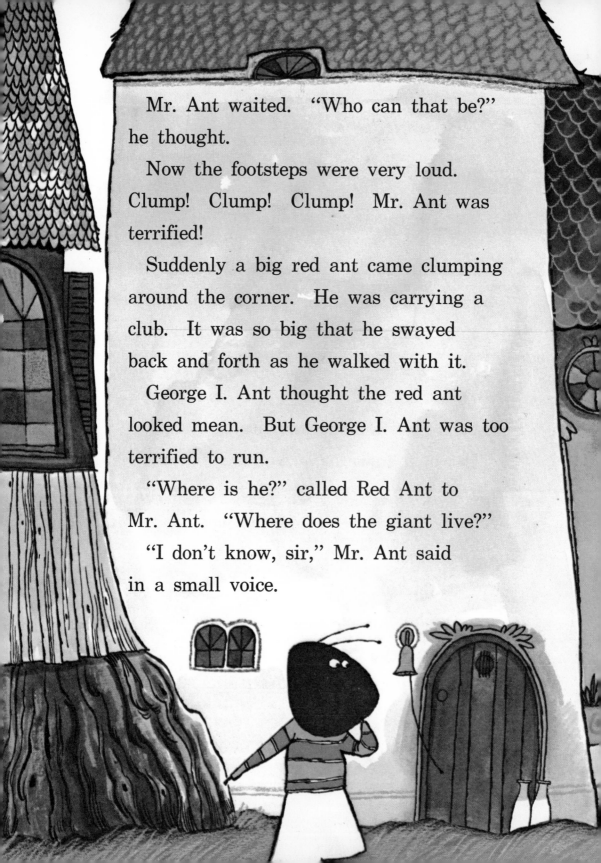

Mr. Ant waited. "Who can that be?" he thought.

Now the footsteps were very loud. Clump! Clump! Clump! Mr. Ant was terrified!

Suddenly a big red ant came clumping around the corner. He was carrying a club. It was so big that he swayed back and forth as he walked with it.

George I. Ant thought the red ant looked mean. But George I. Ant was too terrified to run.

"Where is he?" called Red Ant to Mr. Ant. "Where does the giant live?"

"I don't know, sir," Mr. Ant said in a small voice.

"Don't be afraid," said Red Ant.
"I'll find him and kill him. I'm
carrying a big club. I'm a giant killer.
I have come to kill the giant, but I
won't hurt you."

"Thank you, sir," said Mr. Ant.

"I must find that giant," Red Ant
said as he shook his big club. "But he
won't be hard to find. He has the
biggest house in town."

"Oh, no!" cried Mr. Ant. But Red Ant
didn't hear him. He went on his way,
carrying the club. Mr. Ant ran along
behind him.

They came closer and closer to the
biggest house on the anthill. "Sir, no
giant lives there," Mr. Ant called out
in a small voice.

"Yes, he does," said Red Ant.

The big red ant swayed back and forth
as he went on clumping up the street.
Little Mr. Ant ran along behind him.

"What makes you think a giant lives
there?" asked Mr. Ant.

"My neighbors told me so," said
Red Ant. "And they want me to kill him!
I'm a giant killer, you know."

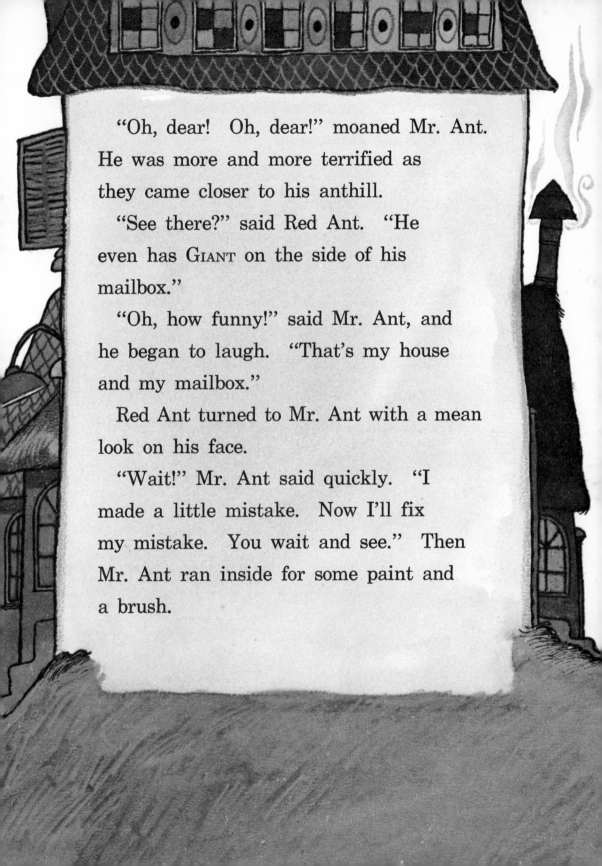

"Oh, dear! Oh, dear!" moaned Mr. Ant.
He was more and more terrified as
they came closer to his anthill.

"See there?" said Red Ant. "He
even has GIANT on the side of his
mailbox."

"Oh, how funny!" said Mr. Ant, and
he began to laugh. "That's my house
and my mailbox."

Red Ant turned to Mr. Ant with a mean
look on his face.

"Wait!" Mr. Ant said quickly. "I
made a little mistake. Now I'll fix
my mistake. You wait and see." Then
Mr. Ant ran inside for some paint and
a brush.

Soon Mr. Ant came back to the mailbox.
He took the brush and put two
dots in his name. With the dots,
it looked like this: G.I.ANT

"That stands for my name—George I.
Ant," he said. "Now I know why your
neighbors were upset. They thought I
was a giant."

"Well, you're not a giant," said
Red Ant. "You are the smallest ant
I ever saw. Why do you need this big
anthill?"

"My wife and our thirty children are coming soon," Mr. Ant told him. "Do you think the neighbors will be more friendly now?"

"They will," answered Red Ant. "It's a nice town. Still, it's too bad there isn't a giant!"

After that, Mr. Ant always wrote George I. Ant when he had to write his name.

Think about This:

What was George I. Ant's mistake?

What parts of the story were make-believe?

What parts could really have happened?

233

Ants Live Here

Ants live here
by the curb stone,
see?
They worry a lot
about giants like
me.

by Lilian Moore

unpack   unkind   unload

unhappy

graph   dolphin   photograph

elephant

germ   gym   magic

giraffe

also   although   altogether

almost

alike   aside   ashore

awhile

forty   north   organ

popcorn

sight   sigh   knight

sighed

clapped   spotted   grinning

trotted

Dexter

Popcorn Dragon

Dexter was a small green dragon. He had tiny wings and short legs. When he was unhappy, fire came out of his mouth.

One day Dexter had no one to play with, so he was unhappy. He sighed a deep sigh. But when he sighed, it wasn't fire that came from his mouth. It was a cloud of smoke!

"I'm blowing smoke!" cried Dexter, and he ran to show his mother. "I didn't know I could do that," he told her. Then he blew more smoke.

"I'm going to show the other animals," he said. And off he went, blowing smoke all the way.

Dexter met the elephant, the giraffe, and the zebra. They watched him blow smoke. Their eyes almost popped out of their heads!

Soon the giraffe said, "Good-by, I have to go now." He slipped away and hid behind a rock. He tried to blow smoke like Dexter. But he couldn't do it.

"Well, good-by," said the elephant. "I have to go, too." He trotted into the woods, trying to blow smoke like Dexter. But he couldn't blow smoke at all.

Then the zebra ran off over a hill and tried to blow smoke. He tried many times, but he couldn't do it.

After a while the zebra, the giraffe, and the elephant came back to watch Dexter again.

"I can blow smoke, and you can't," Dexter said. And he trotted around, showing off.

"Now I think I'll blow smoke rings awhile!" shouted Dexter. He put his head up in the air and blew smoke rings.

"That Dexter thinks he's so smart," said the zebra.

"We don't like him, do we?" asked the giraffe.

"No, we don't! Let's go!" said the elephant.

When Dexter saw the animals going,
he stopped blowing smoke rings.

"Want me to come with you?" he called.

"No, we don't like to watch you
show off," said the giraffe.

So Dexter sighed a big sigh and
went home by himself.

"I don't have anything to do," Dexter
said to his mother.

"Blow some smoke," said his mother.

"I don't feel like it," said Dexter.

"Why not play awhile with the other
animals?" asked his mother.

"They won't play with me," said Dexter.

"Then you must have been showing off,"
his mother said, with a sigh.

Dexter was sorry about showing off.
So he went into a field of tall corn
and sat down to think about it. But
soon he fell asleep.

Later a funny noise woke Dexter.
Pop, pop! Pop, pop, pop!

Then there was a good smell, too.

"Popcorn!" cried Dexter. The fire
that came from his mouth had popped
an ear of corn.

Dexter began to eat the popcorn.
When it was almost gone, he saw another
ear of corn. So he blew on it and
popped more popcorn.

The giraffe, the zebra, and the elephant
heard the pop, pop, popping noise. They
put their heads up in the air and went
sniff, sniff. Then all the animals came
to see what made the popping noise and
what smelled so good.

"Have some popcorn?" asked Dexter.

"You ate it all yourself," said the zebra.

"I'll pop some more," said Dexter.
And he popped corn for all the animals.

"A dragon can be very nice when he
isn't showing off," said the giraffe.
"Let's ask Dexter to play with us."

Dexter never showed off again. If he had to blow a cloud of smoke, he always turned his head to one side.

And when the animals were hungry, Dexter popped popcorn for everyone!

Think about This:

What happened to make Dexter a happy dragon?

What did Dexter learn about making friends?

We work with words.

scent scissors

thoughts bought coughing

pulled pushing butcher

fired chasing skater

pedal wooden lesson

page gypsy ginger

easier dried flies

unfair unlock untrue

Sound the words.

scene

brought

pudding

dining

kingdom

magic

stories

unpack

Narrator

Jolly

Sight words.

palace soup

The King and the Cook

243

Cast: Jolly Jo   King Percival
           Maid   Princess Alice
           Page Boy Lord High
           Narrator

Scene 1

Narrator: The day is Monday, and all is quiet in the palace of King Percival. Jolly Jo is walking down the hallway. He calls out in a loud voice.

Jolly Jo: Good afternoon!

Maid: Shhh! Quiet, sir!

Jolly Jo: What's wrong? The palace was filled with happy sounds this morning. Maids were singing, and page boys were laughing. But now it's so quiet. What has happened?

244

Page Boy: The King is eating
his dinner, sir. No one must say
a word!

Maid: You must be very quiet. Not
even Lord High says a word when the
King is dining.

Page Boy: Dinner is the best part of
the day for the King. Nothing upsets
him more than a dinner that isn't just
right. Everyone must be quiet so the
King can think about his food.

Jolly Jo: What will happen if he
doesn't like it?

Maid: The King will turn red in
the face and shout, "Banish that
cook from the kingdom!" Then the first
cook has to go away. The second cook
will become the first cook. The third
cook will become the second cook. And
a new third cook must be brought to
the palace. We have six cooks a week!

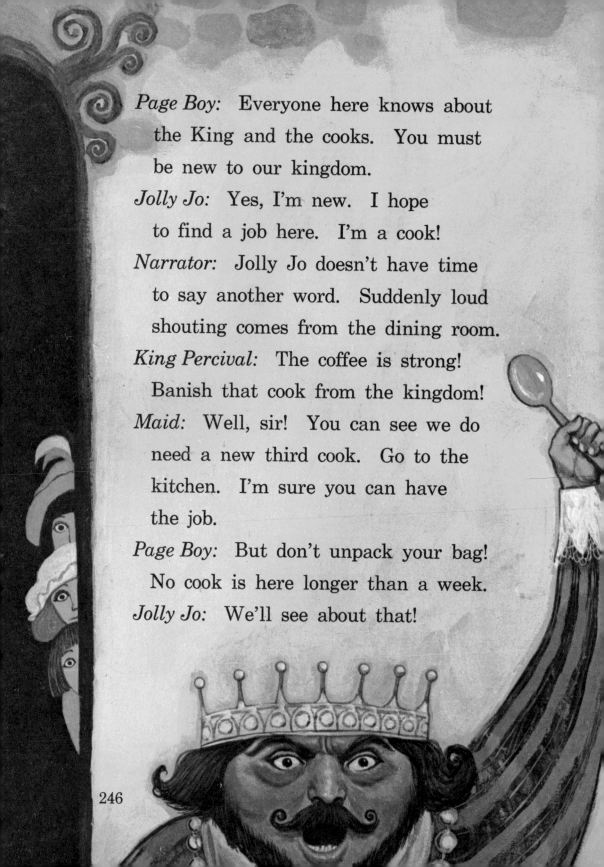

Page Boy: Everyone here knows about
the King and the cooks. You must
be new to our kingdom.

Jolly Jo: Yes, I'm new. I hope
to find a job here. I'm a cook!

Narrator: Jolly Jo doesn't have time
to say another word. Suddenly loud
shouting comes from the dining room.

King Percival: The coffee is strong!
Banish that cook from the kingdom!

Maid: Well, sir! You can see we do
need a new third cook. Go to the
kitchen. I'm sure you can have
the job.

Page Boy: But don't unpack your bag!
No cook is here longer than a week.

Jolly Jo: We'll see about that!

Scene 2

Narrator: The day is Tuesday, and
Jolly Jo is working in the palace
kitchen. Princess Alice is sitting on
a tall stool, talking to him.

Princess Alice: That was a good
story! Thanks, Jolly Jo. I'm glad you
brought so many magic stories with you.
They are the best stories I ever heard.

Jolly Jo: Thank you. I have been
saving stories for a long time.

Princess Alice: Look, they have
taken dinner to Father!

Jolly Jo: Yes, the first cook made
a soup with chicken and noodles.

King Percival: The noodles in this
soup are too long! Banish that cook!

Jolly Jo: Well! I have been here
one day. And now I'm the second cook!
Maybe I should not unpack after all.

Scene 3

Narrator: On Wednesday, Jolly Jo is
working in the palace kitchen as second
cook. Princess Alice is talking to him.

Princess Alice: Have they taken
dinner to my father?

Jolly Jo: Yes, Princess.

Princess Alice: I hope he likes
it! I don't want you to be first cook.
First cooks are always sent away.

Jolly Jo: Don't worry, Princess.
The King is eating his pudding.
It's filled with fine plums brought
from the country. He'll like it!

King Percival: Banish that cook
from the kingdom! There are too many
plums in this pudding!

Princess Alice: No, no! Now you
are first cook, Jolly Jo! And soon
you will be gone.

Jolly Jo: Don't cry, little princess!
Magic won't work when you cry.

Princess Alice: Magic? What magic?

Jolly Jo: I cook with magic! And I
need you to help me. What do
you say?

Princess Alice: Oh yes, Jolly Jo!
I'll do anything you say.

We work with words. | Sound the words.

although   altogether | also

stamped   burned   lighted | cooked

sits   farms   braces | foods

biting   dresses   gladly | happening

takes   lakes   pages | jokes

Scene 4

Narrator: The day is Thursday. The King is about to eat the first dinner cooked by Jolly Jo. He takes the lid from a big dish. He sniffs.

King Percival: What can this be? It's brown and crisp, and it smells great! But how can I eat it if I don't know what it is?

Narrator: The King starts to get up.
  But again he sniffs the food. He sits
  back down.

King Percival: Well, it won't hurt
  to take just one bite. Hmmm. I'll try
  another bite. Hmmm.

Narrator: Soon all the food is gone.
  The King rings a bell, and the page boy
  comes to the table.

King Percival: I wish to see
  Lord High.

Page Boy: I'll bring him to you very
  quickly, King Percival.

Lord High: You called for me, Sir?

King Percival: What did I have for dinner?

Lord High: I don't know, Sir.

King Percival: I don't know what I had! The new cook may be playing jokes on me. In the morning you will eat with me. Together we can try out what the new cook puts on my table.

Scene 5

Narrator: On Friday morning, Jolly Jo is still first cook in the palace.

Princess Alice: I can't believe it! Father ate with Lord High today. They didn't know what they were eating, but both of them liked it. Now Father is having five people to dinner. He used to eat alone. What's happening?

Jolly Jo: My magic is working!

Scene 6

Narrator: Three weeks have gone by.
Jolly Jo is still first cook.

Princess Alice: Jolly Jo! There
are thirty people dining with Father!

Jolly Jo: Yes, Princess. And there
were thirty this morning, also.

Princess Alice: But now I'll worry,
Jolly Jo. You put noodles in the soup,
and I just saw a plum pudding taken
into the dining room. Father knows
about those foods. He'll know if
they are not cooked the way he likes.

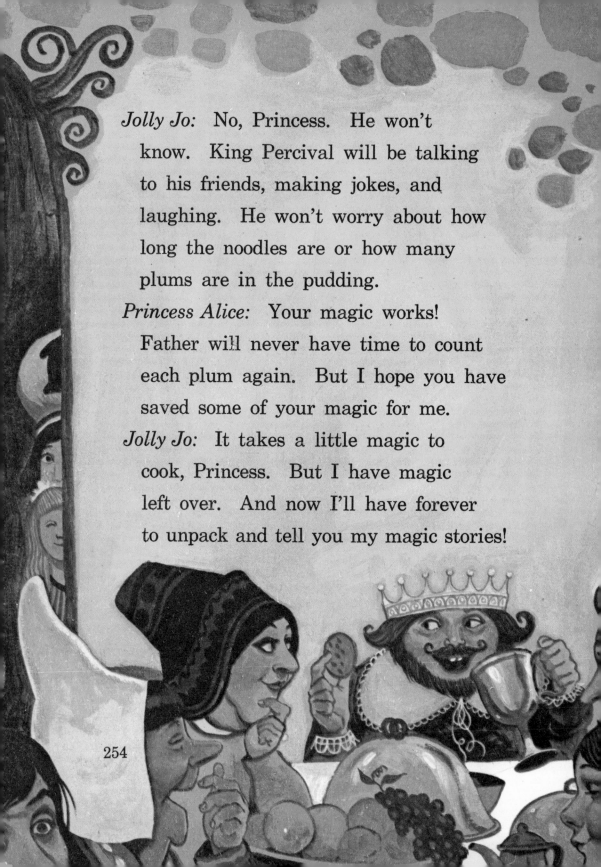

Jolly Jo: No, Princess. He won't
know. King Percival will be talking
to his friends, making jokes, and
laughing. He won't worry about how
long the noodles are or how many
plums are in the pudding.

Princess Alice: Your magic works!
Father will never have time to count
each plum again. But I hope you have
saved some of your magic for me.

Jolly Jo: It takes a little magic to
cook, Princess. But I have magic
left over. And now I'll have forever
to unpack and tell you my magic stories!

ACKNOWLEDGMENTS

Grateful acknowledgment is given for permission to adapt and reprint the following copyrighted material:

"Ants Live Here" by Lilian Moore. Text copyright © 1967 by Lilian Moore from *I Feel the Same Way*. Used by permission of Atheneum Publishers.

"Carlos Goes to the Country" adapted from "Blanco" by Kitty Miller. From *Child Life*, copyright 1969. Used by permission of the publisher.

"City" from *The Langston Hughes Reader* by Langston Hughes. Reprinted by permission of Harold Ober Associates Incorporated. Copyright 1958 by Langston Hughes.

"City Friends" adapted from "The City's Children" by Margaret W. Diemer from *Trailblazer*. The Westminster Press. Used by permission of the author.

"Double Dutch" by Candida Palmer from *Three/Four*, August 10, 1969. Copyright © 1969 by Graded Press. Adapted by permission of the publisher.

"Duchess" from "Duchess and the Sheep" by Mildred M. Bingham. Adapted by special permission from *Jack and Jill* Magazine © 1962 The Curtis Publishing Company.

"A Groundhog by the Fireplace" from "The Groundhog on the Hearth" by Frances B. Watts. Adapted by special permission from *Jack and Jill* Magazine © 1963 The Curtis Publishing Company.

"Ida Lewis" adapted from "Idawalley Lewis" by Joanna Strong and Tom B. Leonard. Reprinted with permission of publishers. © Sayre Publishing, Inc., New York, N.Y. 10016.

"The King and the Cook" by Harriet Walker. Adapted by special permission from *Jack and Jill* Magazine © 1962 The Curtis Publishing Company.

"Little Jeff" by Bernadine Beatie from *Instructor*, December 1963. Adapted by permission of the author.

"Make Your Own Cloud" adapted from "Humpty Finds Out About a Cloud" by Marvin Farbstein, reprinted from *Humpty Dumpty's Magazine*, © 1967 by the Better Reading Foundation. Permission granted by Parents' Magazine Enterprises, Inc.

"Mr. Ant's Mistake" by Audrey Driggs. Adapted by special permission from *Jack and Jill* Magazine © 1962 The Curtis Publishing Company.

"Mr. McBean's Train" adapted from "The Little Train That Helped" by Helen King Marple. From *Child Life*, copyright 1952. Used by permission of the author.

"Mrs. Goose's Bath" adapted from the book *Mrs. Goose and Three-Ducks* by Miriam Clark Potter. Copyright, 1936, renewal, ©, 1964 by Miriam Clark Potter. Reprinted by permission of J. B. Lippincott Company.

"Mother Skunk's Moving Day" by Mary Peacock. Adapted by special permission from *Jack and Jill* Magazine © 1964 The Curtis Publishing Company.

"My Dad Shears Sheep" from "My Father Is a Sheepshearer" by Debora Palmer. Adapted by special permission from *Jack and Jill* Magazine © 1968 The Curtis Publishing Company.

"Off and Away" from *Street Poems* by Robert Froman. Copyright © 1971 by Robert Froman. Reprinted by permission of the publishers, Saturday Review Press/E. P. Dutton & Co., Inc.

255

ILLUSTRATORS

Gus Colichidas, Jim Cummins, Bill England, Bob Gumpertz, Lowell Herrero, Tom Hill, David Kerr, Rebecca Lusk, William Mathison, Lyle Miller, Carol Newsom, Bill Simon, Philip Smith, Frank Stanton, Floyd Webb.